A SKIFF FOR
ALL SEASONS

A SKIFF FOR ALL SEASONS

HOW TO BUILD AN ALASKAN SKIFF

Renn Tolman

with photographs by Melon Purcell

INTERNATIONAL MARINE

CAMDEN, MAINE

To Mary Griswold, whose editorial help
spared me public embarrassment.

Published by International Marine, an imprint of TAB Books.
TAB Books is a division of McGraw-Hill, Inc.

10 9 8 7 6 5 4 3 2

Library of Congress Cataloging-in-Publication Data
Tolman, Renn.
    A skiff for all seasons: how to build the Alaskan skiff/Renn
Tolman; with photographs by Melon Purcell.
        p.   cm.
    Includes index.
    ISBN 0-87742-292-3
    1. Skiffs—Design and construction. 2. Boatbuilding.
        I. Title.
VM355.T65 1992   92-30392
623.82'02—dc20   CIP

Edited by Jim Babb and Donald Casey.
Text Design by James F. Brisson.
Production by Molly Mulhern.
Composition by Watermark Design, Camden, Maine.
Film output and printing by Fairfield Graphics, Fairfield,
Pennsylvania.

Contents

Introduction

My first boat when I moved to coastal Alaska in 1971 was a full-blooded, double-ended dory, powered by an outboard motor located in a well almost amidships. Although wonderfully seaworthy, it was the slowest boat on Kachemak Bay, refusing to climb up on top of the water and plane, even with 18 horsepower. I soon tired of being passed twice a trip, coming and going, by every other boat on the Bay and I sold the dory.

Two impressions remained strong: the dory with its sweeping sheerline was a wonderful boat to look at, and its high bow and flaring sides could handle almost any seas with ease. But the dory's lack of speed made it clear I needed a boat with a different hull shape, one with a broad stern and a rear-mounted motor—in short, a skiff.

Finding that used skiffs in the area were either too expensive or waterlogged tubs, I decided to build my own. Like so many first-time skiff builders looking for a simple design, I chose the Carolina Dory Skiff. This was a very different kind of dory from my double-ender but its flaring sides still qualified it to have dory in its name. The finished boat did give me the speed I wanted—two and a half times, with the same power, that of the old dory—but the real benefit from constructing this first skiff was learning the advantages of epoxy, then a new material for boatbuilding. Epoxy saturation permanently sealed the wood against rot and kept the hull from soaking up water and becoming heavy.

Despite the speed improvement, I was soon dissatisfied with my new skiff. Exceedingly narrow in the bow and with a bottom completely flat fore-and-aft, this design gave the boat a "chin" that acted like a keel. At cruising speed, particularly in following seas, this chin could make the boat yaw violently enough to throw you overboard if you weren't alert.

I thought a local skiff design, the Cook Inlet Dory, showed promise of correcting this problem, so my partner Mary built one. Copying a Cook Inlet Dory built by a local fisherman, Mary improved on the original by using epoxy and fiberglass cloth over the plywood. The new skiff handled much better than the Carolina Dory Skiff, but the greatest improvement was its full-length spray rails, a feature borrowed from a design known as the Oregon Dory. For the first time we had a dry boat, at least in moderate wind.

By 1981 we had become part-time professionals, turning out a few skiffs when orders came and time permitted. It was fun but not very profitable because of the time required to apply the epoxy. By then it was also becoming clear that people really wanted a bigger skiff, one that could handle heavy loads, big motors, and rough seas. The flat bottom of a larger skiff would need to be at least five feet wide, requiring the support of many closely-spaced ribs. Epoxy-saturating all this additional wood would add many construction hours and, effective as epoxy was, the market couldn't support a higher-priced skiff.

The solution to this problem lay literally around the corner, at the boatshop of life-long boatbuilder George Hamm. By then George was building only fiberglass boats, but during the 1960s his shop had turned out nearly a hundred plywood boats ranging from skiffs to 36-foot-long fishing boats. These high-quality boats were unusual in that none had ribs but were made by a simpler method known as bulkhead-and-stringer construction. George had been generous with advice and support during my early days as a boatbuilder and along the way had offered me the use of a jig, a relic of the 60s, on which he had built dozens of fast-to-build, ribless skiffs.

One day a skiff customer came by and I thought that if I could get him to agree to buy a skiff built on George Hamm's jig, I could complete the woodwork quickly enough to epoxy-saturate it and still make money. The customer agreed, and I went to collect the jig only to find George had used it three days earlier to make a mold to build his skiff in fiberglass. There were no hard feelings, but what to do? The customer, a friend and former neighbor, suggested I design him a similar boat from scratch.

I never really liked George's original design, so to improve on it I raised the bow, increasing the sheer, and added dory flare to the sides. Numerous other changes included some minor structural ones, but basically the construction was George's and the design mine. Others who saw the boat liked it and it soon became both popular and profitable.

In Alaska, boats are more often named for their builders than for their place of origin, and these boats gradually became known as Tolman Skiffs. Because I sold so many of them, I flattered myself by thinking the flat-bottom Tolman Skiff was the end-all in skiff design evolution, capable of refinement but complete in concept. But it wasn't long before a customer asked if I could build him a vee-bottom skiff like the beauty he had seen recently in Kodiak, and I had to admit that I couldn't. My discomfort was increased by the knowledge that a local aluminum shop was building just such a boat, and customers who bought them were quick to say they would never go back to a flat bottom. Clearly, if I wanted to consider my skiff in the forefront of skiff design, I had to build one with a vee bottom—but how?

The answer was stitch-and-glue construction.

While there were plenty of vee-bottom plywood boats around, all of them had ribs and some form of longitudinal framing as well. But with the stitch-and-glue technique (developed in England in the 1960s), the plywood panels are held together temporarily with twisted loops of soft wire, called stitches, then bonded permanently with a putty-like mixture of epoxy and filler overlaid with epoxy-saturated strips of fiberglass cloth. This is much like welding sheets of metal and, like a weld, the joint is stronger than the panels it joins. A boat made this way needs little internal reinforcement.

As I focused on stitch-and-glue construction, other problems arose. The bottom panels of a vee-bottom boat, particularly one with a shallow vee like I had in mind, must be bent radically to achieve the desired shape. Traditional construction used thin, easily-bent plywood reinforced with an elaborate internal framework, but it was the framework I was out to eliminate. Compensating for the loss of strength would call for thicker plywood, but how could I get the thicker panels to bend without breaking?

I looked for plans for such a boat in all the usual places and read every relevant book and magazine article for a solution—without success. There were lots of stitch-and-glue designs and lots of vee-bottom designs, but apparently no one had seen fit to combine the two. My solution, neither new nor complicated, was to laminate two thin, easily-bent layers of plywood in place of the single stiff layer.

There were other hurdles to overcome, such as how to keep the curved laminates in firm contact while the epoxy cured, but by 1984 all the technical details had been worked out and we built a prototype, which was the flat-bottom Tolman Skiff unchanged except for the vee bottom. The result was gratifying. Not only was the inside of the boat devoid of framing except for two longitudinal stringers, but it did what vee-bottoms do best: it cut the waves. There was still a bit of tinkering to do, but we now had all the essentials of a proper skiff.

Ironically, it took months to find a customer willing to risk his money on a boat that, without the accustomed internal reinforcement, looked so insubstantial. Eventually the first boat was bought by a former Carolina Dory Skiff builder and owner, who doubtless thought any reasonable risk was worth taking. . . .

For you, the risk is far less.

Today, nearly a decade later, the Tolman Skiff has proved itself in both recreational and commercial use, continuing to attract new owners and to satisfy old ones. What follows are step-by-step instructions for building this versatile skiff and for customizing it to fit your specific needs—a difficult task, at best, with a stamped-out boat. Along the way you will learn a great deal about epoxy saturation and stitch-and-glue construction. If you follow my guidance and you exercise a certain level of care, you will end up with a very fine boat indeed.

Perhaps you'll even go pro. (Resist the urge; it's a likely recipe for economic disaster.) At the very least, you'll be able to modify and repair your skiff down the line. And since there seems to be no practical limit to the lifespan of these skiffs, you'll create a lasting investment. Keep that in mind when you're up to your ears in epoxy.

Introduction

1 | A Proper Skiff

The Tolman Skiff is what I would call a "proper skiff." Any plywood skiff that makes this claim should have six basic characteristics. First, it should reflect its dory origins by having a high bow, a sweeping sheerline, and flaring sides. But unlike its dory ancestors it should have a vee bottom. It should be completely saturated with epoxy resin and

Figure 1-1. A skiff for work . . . and for play.

covered, at least in part, by fiberglass cloth set in epoxy. It should have the main elements of its supporting framework running lengthwise, not crosswise. It should be put together by a method known as stitch-and-glue construction (also called sewn-seam or chineless construction). And last, it should have a means of knocking down the spray generated by a moving hull.

Design

A Tolman Skiff has a *hard-chined, planing, semi-vee* hull. Hard-chined means bottom and sides meet at a hard angle. (This transition could be rounded, as in a soft-chined, or round-bilged boat.) Planing means the boat travels on top of the water, not in it, and implies relatively high speed. (Its counterpart is a displacement hull, designed to travel in the water and slowly.) To understand what is meant by semi-vee you need to know that hard-chined, planing hulls range in a scale from *flat* to *deep vee*.

Semi-vee Hull

Flat bottoms are just that, although they might show a slight turn-up or even some vee toward the bow. Vee bottoms make an angle, called *deadrise*, with the horizontal plane when viewed from the stern or bow. A boat is arbitrarily said to have a deep-vee hull when its angle of deadrise is from 17 to 21 degrees at the transom and remains unchanged throughout most of the length of its bottom to where the bottom surfaces join the bow. A semi-vee hull has an angle of deadrise that increases from stern to bow. On a Tolman Skiff this angle is 8 degrees at the transom, 12 degrees amidships, and becomes that of a deep-vee at the bow.

The greater the angle of deadrise, the more comfortably a boat rides, which begs the question why doesn't a Tolman Skiff have a deep-vee hull? Because comfort comes at a price. Getting deep-vees to plane requires larger motors, which are heavy and

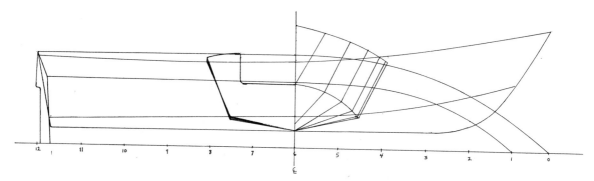

Figure 1-2. The Tolman Skiff lines.

expensive—at odds with the desirable skiff qualities of lightness and economy. A light skiff with a deep vee would be unstable, i.e., tippy, when not moving. Deep-vees have deep draft, which limits their use in shallow water where skiffs are often required to operate. Last, if the angle of deadrise is so great that walking on the inner surface of a boat's hull is impossible, an inner deck becomes necessary; but inner decks are expensive to build and add weight, and should be an option in a skiff, not a necessity. Thus the deep-vee hull, so common in runabouts and cabin-cruisers, is out of place in skiff design.

At the other end of the scale, the flat bottom offers the shallowest draft and the lowest power requirements of any planing hull form. Early Tolman Skiffs had flat bottoms, but offsetting the advantages of a flat bottom is the enormous disadvantage of the rough ride it affords, rarely admitted to by designers and builders. There is a joke about the three most-often-told lies. To them I can add a fourth: that a flat-bot-

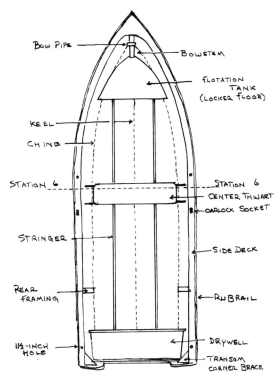

Figure 1-3. Looking down from the top.

tomed skiff will ride softly if its bottom is very narrow, or is turned up in front, or is built this way or that way. In any discussion of how a boat rides, you must remember that external factors, such as the speed of the boat, the height of the waves and their direction, and how heavily the boat is loaded, are at least as important as hull design. Since some of these factors can be controlled by the boat's operator, evaluating a boat's ride is complicated and subjective, and no aspect of boat design is more controversial. Perhaps I can say a vee-bottomed Tolman Skiff rides reasonably well if speed is reduced in rough seas. I can say with more assurance that its ride is a vast improvement over that of any skiff with a flat bottom.

Consequences of a rough ride can be more than mere discomfort; a flat-bottomed boat driven hard can be pounded apart unless—and sometimes even if—it is built very strongly. Such strengthening generally means added weight, cancelling a flat bottom's inherent efficiency. By contrast, a vee bottom is a naturally strong shape (fold a piece of paper and observe its increased stiffness), and plywood bent into the convex shape it must assume at the bow and then laminated, as in a Tolman Skiff, further increases its strength. Thus the vee-bottomed Tolman Skiff, which is identical to its flat-bottomed

A Proper Skiff

predecessor in every other respect, can be built lighter. The power requirements of the two boats are virtually the same.

Because its bottom is fairly flat at the stern, rising only 4¼ inches from horizontal, the vee-bottomed Tolman Skiff has only about three more inches of draft than did the flat-bottomed version. The vee bottom has a shallow enough draft to permit landing on beaches where the gradient is moderate and the surf is not too high. For flat beaches with big surf—the Oregon beaches come to mind—where it is necessary for a skiff to ride the outwash of a wave up the beach for safety, probably a flat-bottomed boat is a necessity. Likewise, in rivers shallow enough to require motors equipped with jet pumps (which project no deeper than the bottom of the boat's hull) a flat-bottomed boat makes sense.

I conclude that if rapid transportation in deep water and potentially rough seas is your primary boating need, a deep-vee hull is best. If the ultimate in shallow water capability is your priority, something with a flat bottom is a necessity. But for the widest variety of boating situations a semi-vee hull is a worthwhile compromise.

Flared Sides

The flaring sides of a Tolman Skiff, which reflect its dory ancestry, make an angle that averages 23 degrees from the vertical and are much easier to evaluate than is the amount of vee in the bottom. Flair provides reserve buoyancy, a term that means the more a boat is tipped the harder tipping becomes, and thus resists capsizing. If you are an average recreational boater, you might think capsizing an unlikely danger, but consider this incident. On a recent, sunny, summer afternoon, four men left the local boat harbor in a Boston Whaler, a design whose vertical sides afford no reserve buoyancy. As they rounded the point near the harbor entrance, they encountered the short, steep waves of a strong tidal current opposed by a stiff day breeze. The Whaler, catching the waves on its beam, flipped bottom-side-up. Do I have to add that Alaskan waters are too cold for swimming? Although poor boat handling was certainly involved in this accident, reserve buoyancy would have provided a margin of safety.

Figure 1-4. Flair and deadrise. (Seam details are shown in Figure 1-5.)

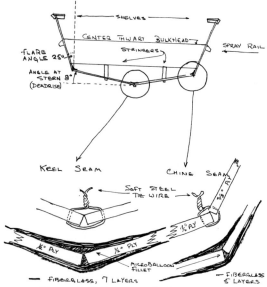

Figure 1-5. Stitch-and-glue construction.

Flaring sides also enable a small, dory-style boat to carry a big load. An empty Tolman Skiff has a beam at the waterline of a bit more than 5 feet; the beam grows to 7 feet at the gunwale. As the skiff is loaded, the waterline width rapidly increases because loading sinks the boat deeper in the water. You could say the boat grows as it is loaded. But as the load is increased the rate at which the boat sinks decreases. Technically stated, the rate of immersion slows as loading increases.

The practical consequence of this immersion principle is that a Tolman Skiff can be heavily loaded and still maintain good freeboard, a term defined as the height of a boat's side above the surface of the water. Of course, freeboard is what keeps the water out. Two commercial salmon fishermen in Alaska demonstrated this principle by loading their Tolman Skiff with 2½ tons—5,300 pounds, to be exact—of salmon plus their nets. A snapshot shows that even with this load, which is far heavier than I would recommend, their freeboard was reduced by only about one half. We recreational boaters have our confidence in the boat built up by stories like this.

High Bow

A Tolman Skiff has a hull depth of a full 4 feet at the bow to enable it to ride over and deflect large waves. I have taken solid green water over the bow in my skiff only once—coming off a beach in heavy surf. In short, steep seas, however, small jets of water sometimes squirt through the two holes for the bowline located just under the gunwale, a good indicator that the bow is none too high. (This relatively high bow restricts the operator's vision somewhat, and I strongly recommend steering the boat from a standing position, unless the water is calm and you are going slowly.)

There is an additional benefit to the high bow. Joining it with the relatively low freeboard amidships creates a sweeping sheerline, giving the Tolman Skiff lines that many have admired. I think part of the pleasure of owning a boat, like owning a car, comes from its looks. And why not? Good looks are free.

But first, there is work to be done.

2 | Design Choices

In General . . .

One of the advantages of building your own skiff is being able to choose some of the features you want. You can make some choices, like seating and storage, after you build the hull and roll it over, when maybe you can get better picture what you want. But other decisions are what I'd call structural; that is, they have to do with the hull itself.

Figure 2-1. Design choices are reflected in the finished boat.

Before you set saw to wood, there are several structural decisions you'll have to make, such as how long you'll make your skiff, what kind of transom to build (which depends on your choice of power), and what sort of center bracing you'll put in the hull.

Choosing the Length

The 18-footer?

You can make your skiff 18 or 20 feet long (or any length in between). The 18-foot skiff is as wide and deep as the 20-footer, but it has a 2-foot section removed between the middle and stern. It is as if you cut the skiff crossways, like a loaf of bread, and took out a 2-foot slice. Taking out this slice makes the skiff about 50 pounds lighter and $75 cheaper to build.

The shorter skiff has the advantage of better maneuverability, which might help if you dock it in tight places. Less length also lets you trailer it more easily, particularly when parking it. Perhaps you'd choose the shorter skiff if you keep your boat in a marina that charges by the foot. Or you might choose the smaller skiff simply because you don't usually carry heavy loads or lots of people. And while smaller boats are always less seaworthy than larger ones, other things being equal, that can be a minor consideration if you do your boating on small or protected bodies of water.

Or the 20-footer?

For use on large bodies of water, where the crests of the waves are farther apart, the longer skiff has a definite advantage. Even two additional feet of length makes the boat bridge the wave crests better, reducing the rocking-horse motion called pitching. Pitching is uncomfortable, particularly for the passengers, who have nothing to do but sit there and suffer. My partner and I make ocean skiff trips, some as long as 1,000 miles, and we were pleasantly surprised at how much smoother the ride was when we sold our 18-foot skiff and built a 20-footer. Since discomfort contributes to fatigue, which in turn affects safety, we figured we benefited in that respect as well.

Pitching also affects performance. As the skiff pitches, it tends to bury its bow in the waves, which slows it down. When it slows, it drops off plane and the motor has to work hard to get the skiff back on plane again. In spite of its greater weight (about seven percent), I think the longer skiff is more efficient running in rough conditions than the shorter one.

The heavier 20-foot skiff is likewise more efficient for carrying heavy loads than an 18-footer. The two extra feet of length in the 20-foot skiff are back where the bottom has the least vee and where the skiff gets the lift that makes it plane. A heavily-loaded 18-

footer sinks deeper into the water and requires more power to plane. So when choosing which length skiff to build, carefully gauge the load you intend to carry most often.

Everything considered, I think the 20-foot skiff is a better all-around boat than the 18-footer. Go for the 20-footer unless you have very specific reasons why only an 18-foot skiff will do.

Power Needs

Before getting into transom design, which is a matter of the number of motors and their placement, let's look at how much power you need. Although Tolman Skiff owners have used motors from 18 to 110 horsepower, most, including me, use motors between 40 and 70 horsepower. A 30-horsepower motor will plane an 18-foot skiff with a small load (three people and gear) at 20 miles per hour, but the motor has to run at wide-open throttle to do it. This is hard on the motor and burns a lot of fuel besides. With 40 horsepower you can run at the same speed with the same load but with the throttle setting reduced. The motor isn't straining and the fuel economy is improved. Alone in the skiff you could expect a top speed approaching 30 miles per hour.

Still, most owners I talk to who run their skiffs with 40 horsepower motors say they would go bigger if they repowered. I think the main reason they want more power is because of poor performance when their skiffs are loaded heavily, not because they are looking for a higher top speed. A Tolman Skiff is a big boat but it's light, so there's a tendency to power it with too small a motor. But like a pickup truck, a roomy skiff provides the opportunity to load it very heavily with people, fish, lumber, or whatever. There's plenty of room to double the load of the 18-foot skiff in my example above, to six people and their gear, but a 40-horsepower motor would then be working just as hard as the 30-horsepower motor was with three aboard. When you choose your power, the question you should ask yourself is how much weight you plan to carry most of the time.

A Simple Calculation

A national boating trade association has published a power guideline for outboard-powered boats that I think is useful. They say one horsepower for every 25 pounds of gross weight is ideal, and one horsepower for every 40 pounds is minimum. Let's plug some actual figures into this rule and see how it works out. If you were to run a 50-horsepower motor on your Tolman Skiff, you'd ideally have a gross weight, that is, the skiff, motor, gas, etc., plus the load that's in it, of no more than 1,250 pounds. You could increase the load until the gross weight was 2,000 pounds and still expect the motor to plane the skiff. A Tolman Skiff weighs close to 700 pounds, a motor in the 50-horsepower range weighs about 200 pounds, and two 6-gallon gas tanks weigh about 40 pounds each, for a total of about 1,000 pounds, so you could say your net weight—passengers, gear, etc.—should fall between 250 and 1,000 pounds.

Personal experience has shown me that this range of loading is a reasonable expectation for a motor of this size. I run my skiff with a 55-horsepower motor. According to the guidelines my gross weight should fall between 1,375 and 2,200 pounds. I can fill my skiff with people and gear—and throw in a couple of dogs—and still go 20 miles per hour with the throttle two-thirds open (the most economical setting). On some of our long trips we've carried camping gear, a month's supply of food, and 55 gallons of gas. Add to this a spare motor, spare parts, guns, fishing tackle, and all the other miscellaneous items we need for wilderness travel, and our gross weight exceeded a ton, I'm sure, but the skiff still planed at less than full throttle.

Transom Design

Unlike a factory-built boat, whose transom is built the same no matter what the power, the transom of a Tolman skiff can be custom made. It can be cut out wide for two motors of equal size or given a narrow cut-out for a single motor. If you are a commercial fisherman, perhaps you want one motor offset so you can set a net over the other side of the transom. You have many choices. The first thing to ask yourself is do you want to power your skiff with two equal-sized motors or a single one.

Twins?

Some skiff owners choose to power with two equal-sized motors to have a backup in case one motor fails. Others object, saying that if the two motors are small, in the 20- to 30-horsepower range, and the skiff is heavily loaded, one motor alone won't plane it. They also point out two small motors burn more fuel than one large one of the same horsepower.

To overcome the first objection some owners have powered their skiffs with two motors in the 40- to 50-horsepower range. I'm not very happy with this solution because I think it's simply too much iron hanging off the stern, which lowers the freeboard and has a bad effect on trim and handling. But I'll have to admit these owners report few bad effects, and some of them have made impressive trips in their skiffs.

As for the second objection to two equal-sized motors, there doesn't appear to be a solution. Expect poorer fuel economy from twin power, probably because smaller propellers are less efficient and because two motors increase the underwater drag.

It is, of course, possible to run two motors at the stern with tillers, as I and others have done. But believe me, when you're going fast and find yourself unexpectedly in shoal water, it's a real circus act trying to get both motors slowed down and tilted before you wreck them on the bottom. Most will find it easier to link twin motors together and control them with remote steering, shifts, and throttles. This means you have to build some sort of steering station. A remote steering station often leads to power tilt and trim and self-starting with all their extra weight, expense, and complication.

Or a Single Motor?

If you do decide on two motors for your main power, building your transom is straightforward, and you'll find the dimensions and construction described in Chapter 8. Planning a transom for a single motor is more complicated, requiring more than simply adequate room for the motor to turn. Increasingly these days, skiff owners want a small auxiliary motor—usually from six to 15 horsepower—in addition to the main motor. This auxiliary, or kicker as it is usually called, is often mounted on a transom bracket. These are sold ready-made and have a lever mechanism to raise and lower the motor. If you want to mount your kicker this way, making a narrow cutout for your main motor (detailed in Chapter 8) will provide adequate space on the back of your transom to bolt on the bracket.

Figure 2-2. Wide transom cutout to accommodate twin motors. Note net skiff has binboards, bulkheads, and rounded gunwales.

If you mount your kicker on a bracket, it is hard to steer it and to control the shift and throttle because you have to reach over the top of the transom. Many skiff owners leave the main motor down and steer with it when running their kicker. They report this works well, but there must be some loss of efficiency due to the drag of the lower unit of the main motor, and they still have the problem of reaching the shift and throttle. There is also the problem of draft: the main motor draws much more water than does the kicker, especially since you can run kickers in a shallow-water-drive position.

If you want to tilt the main motor and actually steer your skiff with your kicker, you can mount it beside your main motor in a wide transom cutout; but with your main motor centered, your kicker will have to be pushed so close to the outer edge of the cutout that its steering range will be limited. You can reach the kicker's shift and throttle more easily than if it were mounted on a bracket, but you may still be steering with the main.

Figure 2-3. Transom-mounted and bracket-mounted auxiliary outboards. Note the different features of the two skiffs.

The solution to full steering for your transom-mounted kicker is to mount your main slightly off-center, which gives each motor the space to turn fully without hitting the other. For me this is the perfect setup. I like to troll with my kicker and run it in water too shallow for my main. When I tilt the main motor and slide my movable seat over to run the kicker, the main motor cover becomes a comfortable backrest. Let me assure you there's no tendency for the offset main motor to push the skiff in circles, and since the kicker is further off-center than the main, they come close to balancing each other out. The biggest disadvantage seems to be looks. Although it doesn't bother me, I've had only limited success selling this idea to Tolman Skiff customers.

Motor Wells

Old skiff hands among you will doubtless be surprised that I don't offer motor wells as a transom option. Mounting the motor forward of the transom in a well is supposed to increase seaworthiness. Waves overtaking the stern of the skiff are deflected by the high, uncut transom. Although part of the wave can enter the well through a cutout in the bottom of the transom, it doesn't overflow into the skiff because the stern, not weighted down by a motor, is more buoyant. And the motor, being well inside the boat, is protected from waves breaking over it.

While all this may be true, it is also true that well-designed skiffs with motors mounted on their transoms are also seaworthy, providing—and this is very important—that they have effective drywells to contain and remove any water that comes in over the cut-out transoms. (A second alternative is a self-bailing deck inside the skiff, which would also remove the water.) As for the motor, today's well-sealed outboards can stand being briefly dunked by waves.

If the advantages of motor wells are debatable, the drawbacks are not. Wells remove a big area from the bottom of the hull, thus reducing the planing surface: expect a skiff with a well to require more power and use more fuel. Efficiency is further reduced by the turbulence a well creates. Some wells "pump" with certain motors; that is, they splash water on board, which has to be controlled with spray deflectors. Likewise, motors mounted in wells often cavitate during turns when they can't get sufficient water to their props. And a well takes up a lot of usable space in the skiff. I could go on and on.

Figure 2-4. A motor well.

When I started building skiffs 17 years ago, most skiffs had wells. Gradually they have disappeared except on seine skiffs, where the well serves to keep the net away from the motor. Not only have I not built a skiff with a well for many years, but lately I've had to remove a couple of wells and cut down the transoms. It's a job I don't like, so you won't find a description in this book of how to build wells.

Limbers

Limbers are the boatbuilder's term for the holes cut in a boat's framing to let bilge water collect at the lowest point in the hull. Since the two limbers in a Tolman Skiff are in the bottom of the stringers, they must be cut before the bottom is fastened on. If you plan to leave the area underneath the drywell open, you'll cut the limbers where the stringers meet the transom. But if you want a bulkhead under the drywell to make a flotation tank/storage compartment, you'll want to cut the limbers where the stringers meet the bulkhead.

I like the bulkhead because it provides dry storage space for tools and spare motor

Figure 2-5. Offset motor with bulkhead beneath. Note binboards.

parts close to where you need them. Bilge water collects in front of the bulkhead where it's easy to bail. If you have a bilge pump, as I do, the inlet is easy to get at. And you can still drain the skiff when it's on its trailer by means of a tube that runs through the compartment. However, many skiff owners, particularly those who have consoles for forward steering, like to leave the space under the drywell open for gas tanks and batteries. The console provides the dry storage.

Although the bulkhead under the drywell isn't structural, the limbers are, so now is the time you've got to make the decision whether you want the area open or enclosed. The placement of the limbers will be shown in Chapter 7.

Center Bracing

The Thwart

A Tolman Skiff needs center bracing to take the place of the ribs found in the dinosaurs (as I call traditional skiffs). Center bracing prevents the sides from flexing and ties them to the bottom. A center *thwart* (thwart is a boating term for seat) is the center bracing I most often put in skiffs that aren't going to be used for commercial fishing. It provides seating for three people in the center of the boat where their weight is best distributed. The thwart also adds a 12- x 12- x 54-inch storage locker. If you don't build a center thwart, you'll have to figure out other kinds of seating and storage if you need them. If, as a first-time skiff builder, there's a question in your mind as to how to lay out your skiff, I'd say go ahead and build a center thwart.

Knees

The center thwart does create an obstruction you have to step over when walking from front to back in your skiff. If you want the whole interior completely open and unobstructed, you can build two pairs of knees for center bracing. A knee is an L-shaped piece of ¾-inch plywood fastened to framing on the sides of the skiff. Often owners who want this layout also want a level interior floor. This could be glued in and sealed, in which case I call it a deck, or removable panels, which I call floorboards.

Inner Decks and Floorboards

Since your decision to build knees might depend on whether you want your skiff to have an inner deck or floorboards, here are their pros and cons.

Either a deck or floorboards lets you walk around your skiff without tripping over the two longitudinal stringers, but since the stringers run lengthwise, you already have a walkway nearly 2½ feet wide running from one end of the skiff to the other. You do, however, have to watch your step if you're moving across the skiff—fighting a big fish, for example. And while you might trip on the stringers, they are an advantage as a brace for your feet if you have to lean over the side. They also keep gear such as gas cans, pails, and tackle boxes from traveling around as the skiff bounces through choppy water.

As the bottom of the skiff becomes more deeply veed toward the bow, it becomes harder to walk on. Some skiff owners overcome this by putting floorboards on the stringers forward of the center thwart. I think this is a good compromise. Not only is it already fairly easy to walk around in the back of the boat, but raising the floor behind the center thwart has the effect of lowering the sides, increasing the chance of falling overboard. There is less danger in front of the thwart where the sides rise up quickly toward the bow.

Speaking of safety, I should mention that either a deck or floorboards, by raising the center of gravity and allowing weight to be

Figure 2-6. Inner deck. Note transom cut for single motor.

placed farther from the centerline, makes a light boat with flaring sides like the Tolman Skiff more tippy. I definitely discourage you from building either a deck or floorboards in a skiff in which you intend to carry loads that can slide from side to side. I have heard of decked skiffs capsizing when loaded heavily with fish. For carrying people, handrails on top of the gunwales might be a good idea.

Inner decks in most boats are self-bailing. Water that comes in as spray—or even a wave in the extreme case—goes out the drains without the need to bail or pump. The deck of a Tolman Skiff installed on top of the stringers, which is as high as I think it should be, may or may not be self-bailing, depending on how heavily the skiff is loaded. When it isn't moving, a skiff that has a large motor, a kicker, a couple of gas tanks, and a couple of people in the rear will float at a level where water comes in through the drains. This isn't unsafe because the water will never enter beyond a certain level, but most people find it annoying. Some put the drain plug in when they're not moving. Others equip the drain with a one-way rubber valve. Still others have no deck drain at all; the deck drains into an undecked area, or sump, which can be bailed by hand or with an electric or manual pump.

Whereas a decked skiff may or may not be self-bailing, it is self-tending, which means that rainwater will run out when the skiff is floating at a dock or mooring. Although this seems like a great advantage, you should remember that the smallest electric bilge pump will bail a skiff—even for several weeks—with little battery drain.

Safety is probably the argument most often given for wanting self-bailing decks. (I should point out that the deck in a Tolman Skiff bails if the skiff is planing, no matter what the load.) If the water is rough and the wind is above 20 knots or so, lots of spray will come aboard at certain speeds and on certain headings in relation to the wind. With a deck you can concentrate on steering instead of bailing. However, I find bailing no great problem unless I have to bend over and do it with a container. My skiff is equipped with a manual bilge pump, and a few strokes every few minutes keep up with any amount of spray I've run into. An electric pump would do the same thing. Meanwhile I can keep my eye on the waves and steer to meet them.

Binboards and Bulkheads

In addition to using knees to brace skiffs with floorboards or decks, I use them for center bracing in commercial-fishing skiffs that have fish holds made with *binboards*. Binboards are removable planks held between cleats fastened to the sides of the skiff, and since they give no support, knees are required. In skiffs with binboards I sometimes put the two pairs of knees spaced closely together and notch one binboard to fit on top of them to make a seat. Or the knees might be attached to the cleats that hold the binboards.

A third form of center bracing is one or more fixed bulkheads. These are used to make fish holds in the same way binboards are, but unlike the binboards, bulkheads are fastened to framing members running up and down the sides. One ⅜-inch plywood bulkhead at Station 6, the center of the skiff from front to back, provides enough center bracing if it measures at least 22½ inches high from its lowest point in the center of the vee bottom.

Once you have decided exactly what it is you're building, the next step is to work out exactly how.

3 | Tools and Shop Space

Special boatbuilding tools are not necessary for building a plywood and epoxy skiff—none of the exotic antique tools like slicks or adzes. Nor do you need any of the monstrous cast-iron power tools of old. The tools you do need are almost all common ones you'd use on any plywood project—building kitchen cabinets, for example. If you are not a woodworker already, you can find most of them at your local hardware store, although a few hard-to-find tools may have to be bought mail-order.

Mail-order sources of power tools are often cheaper than local stores, although a local store will sometimes dicker when you show them lower priced competition. A list of tool sources is provided in the Appendix.

Hand Tools

Marking

For measuring and marking you'll need a 25-foot tape measure, a framing (rafter) square, a combination square, a 4-foot thin metal straightedge, a chalk box, a compass, and both a carpenter's pencil and, for making fine, accurate lines, a regular one. Of course there are lots of angles, so you'll need an adjustable bevel square and a simple plastic protractor. A 20-inch or longer level is also essential.

Cutting

You'll need a handsaw. A crosscut with 10 teeth per inch is a good general-purpose tool. Although not necessary, a Japanese saw, with its short blade, is helpful for fine cuts in tight quarters. They are difficult to sharpen so get one with hardened teeth and a throw-away blade. They look as if they might be handy for flipping flapjacks as well.

Shaping

Among edged tools, a 1½- or 2-inch chisel is needed for making cuts in difficult places. I use a sharp hatchet to rough-shape the bowstem, but this job can also be done with a power plane. As for hand planes, leave those long, applewood beauties you bought at the garage sale on the shop wall to show you're a real craftsman. What you need is a low-angle block plane, which you must keep razor sharp.

There are lots of sharpening methods, and any is good if it works for you. Many involve some method of rough grinding at the prescribed angle (12 degrees for this plane), followed by honing the very edge of the blade with a finer abrasive at a slightly steeper angle, but I have never had good luck with this system. I get better results from a fixture that holds the plane (or chisel) blade at a constant angle relative to the sharpening stone. Sharpening proceeds on three stones of progressively finer grits (I use fast-cutting Japanese waterstones), but the sharpening angle remains unchanged. Sharpened this way, my plane will remove a long, curly shaving from end-grain plywood.

Figure 3-1. Sharpening the blade for a low-angle block plane.

A Skiff for all Seasons

Clamping

The other day I saw a picture of a small boat under construction bristling with so many clamps it looked like a porcupine. For the Tolman Skiff, 18 clamps should do the job. If you have to buy them, bar clamps are handier and faster to use than C-clamps. Get a dozen 6-inchers and a half dozen 12-inchers. If you already have lots of C-clamps (or can borrow them), only two really need to be 12-inchers.

Utility

Of course you'll need a hammer. Use whatever you have, but for the 4- to 8-penny nails required in this project a 16-ounce hammer with curved claws is appropriate.

Here's a list of few other hand tools that you will use:

- Awl
- Nail set ($\frac{3}{32}$-inch)
- Hacksaw
- Pry bar
- Adjustable wrench
- Stiff-joint pliers
- Diagonal-cutting pliers
- Screwdrivers (Phillips and straight bit)
- Utility knife
- Large scissors
- Ten-inch nippers

This last item is not so common, but 10-inch nippers, also called carpenter's pincers, are a great tool for pulling nails in general carpentry as well as boatbuilding. On this project they clip the nails used to temporarily hold the planking for fitting. They are available from Silvo Hardware, or Harbor Freight Tools (see Appendix).

Hand sanders, rasps, and scrapers are listed in the section on epoxy finishing tools.

Power Tools

It is difficult to state which power tools you absolutely must have for this project. In fact, you can build the whole boat with only hand tools, but I doubt that many modern builders will want to rip an amount of lumber longer than a football field or drive several hundred screws by hand. Power tools are enormous time savers: working without them can double the 300 hours I estimate the project requires. Also many woodworking operations, if done by hand—cutting tight-fitting joints, for example—require a much higher level of skill to achieve accuracy than if they were done with power tools. Most people, I assume, take pride in such accuracy. (I'll admit, however, that epoxy can fill the sloppiest joint with no loss of quality.)

My list of power tools is the optimum complement, not a required minimum. I favor professional-quality tools, even for the amateur, rather than the cheap ones known as throwaways. I read stories about people who have built whole schooners with $16 drills their mothers-in-law put in their Christmas stockings, but such miraculous things have never happened to me. Of course you can use whatever you have, but if you need to buy, buy the best—it lasts scarcely long enough.

If you choose to buy them, all the tools I list, except the sander/polisher, are basic to a wide variety of construction projects, from homes to doll houses, and therefore can be thought of as long-term investments. I'll tell what they will be used for on this project so you can establish your own priorities if you can't afford all of them.

There are alternatives to buying tools. You can borrow, rent, or . . . I'll stop short of saying steal. You can enroll at your local high school or community college in a woodworking course, many of which are thinly-disguised shop-rentals. You can join an amateur boatbuilder's co-op. Or you can hire a professional wood shop to do some of the more complex woodworking operations.

Drills

It has been said that in boatbuilding you can scarcely have enough electric drills. I have six, mostly to lessen the inconvenience of changing bits. Two will do. They can both be ⅜-inch capacity, variable-speed, reversing models, costing around $65, but a better choice is to make one of them a ½-inch drill, such as the Milwaukee Super Holeshooter ($130). The ½-inch chuck will accommodate ⁷⁄₁₆-inch hole saw arbors and other large drill bits, and the low gearing of ½-inch drills is better for the heavy work of drilling big holes. For me, it is also easier to control a screwdriver bit in these slow-turning drills than in the faster-turning ⅜-inch drills. If you want to go first class, add a Jacobs keyless chuck to your ⅜-inch drill for speedy bit changing.

Cordless drills are a nice luxury, but although quite expensive—typically close to $200 with the mandatory extra battery—many have neither the power nor the speed of even the cheapest plug-in drill. They are also fragile and will roll over and die if dropped or used roughly. Cordless drills of different brands, even with the same specifications, seem to vary widely in performance, so buy one only if you're sure it has the power to handle big drills and the endurance to drive lots of long, large-size screws. Their nicest feature is an adjustable clutch (available on some models) that makes it impossible to drive screws too deep.

For drilling the many holes in a Tolman Skiff that are 1 inch in diameter and larger, I choose hole saws. They cut more smoothly and veer off center less than the ubiquitous paddle (spade) bits do and they cut misplaced or forgotten fastenings without flinching (but not hardened sheetrock screws!). But a hole is a hole; use the bits you've got. You will need 1⅛-, 1⅜-, and 1½-inch sizes and perhaps one or two more, depending upon your choice of options for your particular skiff.

Boatbuilders were among the first to discover that drilling for wood screws was best done with taper-point drills equipped with countersinks, known as Fuller drills (after the primary manufacturer, W. L. Fuller, Inc., see Appendix). There's no shortage of special drills that make tapered screw holes, but all but Fuller drills break, usually sooner rather than later, and particularly in hardwood.

Five sizes of Fuller drills will accommodate all the screw sizes used in a Tolman Skiff. Even though these are all tapping screws, which are theoretically able to thread themselves into the wood without pilot holes, don't be tempted to take this shortcut: pre-drill for all screws. The exception to this will be screws driven through two layers of plywood to hold them in contact while the glue sets. These screws will later be removed. One hardened sheetrock screw broken off in a joint you have to saw through later will make you grumpy all day.

You must order these drills directly from Fuller; the assortment of Fuller drills sold by other mail order tool suppliers is usually sized for hardwood, not the softwood (fir) from which a Tolman Skiff is built. Order the following:

2 ea. ⅛″	Taper point drill			No. 20100125
1 ea. 5/32″	″	″	″	No. 20100156
1 ea. 5/32″	″	″	″	No. 20200156
1 ea. 3/16″	″	″	″	No. 20100187
2 ea. ⅜″	Countersink			No. C5
2 ea. ⅜″	″	″	″	No. C7
1 ea. ⅜″	″	″	″	No. C9

As a cheap but very inefficient alternative to Fuller drills, you can use standard untapered twist drills in the sizes listed above with tape wrapped around their shanks to indicate proper drilling depth, then follow the holes with a conventional countersink.

Saws

I do most of the cutting on this project with a portable electric circular saw, commonly referred to as a Skilsaw (the registered name of the circular saws from Skil Tool Company, Inc.). Cutting gentle curves with a Skilsaw is very fast, easy, and accurate as compared with doing it with other tools. But cutting curves in thick wood eats Skilsaws, and building a Tolman Skiff may be hazardous to the health of saws of less than 12 amps. (By the way, the number of amps capacity of an electric tool is a good rule-of-thumb for rating it: the bigger the number, the better the tool.)

If you don't already own a Skilsaw, or you decide to buy a more powerful saw, I recommend a 7¼-inch wormdrive, a saw that is becoming ever more popular with both pros and amateurs. Because it weighs so much—more than 16 pounds—it presses firmly against the work surface and doesn't slide around like a lighter saw. Yet the wormdrive is so well-balanced you won't object to the extra weight. A long table makes it track well while widely-spaced, well-positioned handles give you positive control. The left-mounted blade lets right-handers better see where it is cutting, and the saw is built for the ruggedest service, including falls from a sawhorse onto concrete. Once expensive, they now cost no more than other 13 amp saws ($130) and are often on sale for less. Although any brand of wormdrive is good, I've heard Black and Decker makes the best.

Equip your Skilsaw with one of the new, thin-rim carbide blades, such as the Piranha by Black and Decker. Choose a 40-tooth combination blade for general cutting. They cut fast, yet they don't splinter plywood, qualities that, until now, have never been combined in a single blade. They are expensive (about $15) but well worth it.

A jigsaw, with its capacity to cut tight curves, will complement your Skilsaw. Many people think of a band saw when they think about the curve-cutting requirements of boatbuilding. A band saw is a wonderful tool and I use one, but it isn't necessary if you have a good jigsaw.

To deliver what it promises, though, a jigsaw must be first-class, like the Bosch Model 1582, about which the company says, without much exaggeration, "Runs like a sewing machine, cuts like a chain saw." The Bosch, with its 1-inch cutting stroke, orbital action, and powerful motor, was the first jigsaw able to cut fast and accurately in thick wood and has been widely copied. All such saws cost about $140.

Planes

There is a large amount of knotty, cross-grained wood to remove when you build a Tolman Skiff. Planing it by hand will turn you into a gorilla, but it's easy with a power plane. Also, a job like planing the long, ever-changing bevels on the stringers requires great skill with a hand plane but is much easier with a power plane. I suggest buying a Bosch Model 3258 or Makita Model 1900BW 3¼-inch power plane (about $100). Neither of these is a wonderful tool because of their short bed length, but it is hardly worth buying a $300 Porter Cable Versaplane to build a single Tolman Skiff. If you want to compromise, you can buy the long bed Makita Model 1100 for about $200.

Routers

All corners of a Tolman Skiff must be well-rounded, both to permit the fiberglass to wrap around without bubbling and to prevent the paint, or even the wood, from wearing—which will soon happen if the corners are left sharp. Also, nothing will contribute so much to the good looks of your finished skiff and reflect so well your skill as a boatbuilder. This is a very challenging job to do neatly and consistently with hand tools, even when aided by a power sander. By far the best way of rounding over, or bullnosing, as boatbuilders call it, is with a router equipped with a ¼-inch carbide rounding-over bit with a ball-bearing guide. A router of minimum power is adequate, but a first-quality tool is essential, such as the Porter Cable Model 100 ($100).

If you decide on a router, also buy a 1-inch flush trimming bit with a ball bearing on its outer end. This bit makes many plywood trimming jobs simple, planing the inside curve of the gunwale, for example, which is devilishly hard to do with a hand plane.

Sanders

I sanded my entire first skiff using only an orbital (palm) sander, and you can too. However, I predict you'll soon become frustrated with how slowly it sands large surfaces and its propensity to clog frequently with epoxy dust. But an orbital sander is indispensable for sanding in tight spots, for sanding into corners without damaging them, and for sanding places like outside corners, which require a delicate touch. Doubtless it does more things well than any other power sander. Many companies make them, none seems better than the rest, and all cost $60 or less.

For speedier sanding of large, open areas the tool of choice is—no, not the belt sander, which burns epoxy and is only comfortable sanding flat surfaces—the sander/polisher with an 8-inch foam pad. (Do not confuse this tool with the *sander/grinder*, a tool identical in appearance but which runs at about 6,000 rpm compared with about 2,000 rpm for the sander/polisher.) The sander/polisher's soft, flexible pad conforms to curved surfaces, and its rotary action keeps it from clogging as often as an orbital. Best of all, on each pass it sands twice the area of an orbital.

At about $140, a top-of-the-line polisher may be too expensive if you are a one-time skiff builder, especially since it is an unusual tool for general woodworking. Thus I will temporarily set aside my contempt for cheap tools and suggest the Wen polisher ($40 from Northern Hydraulics, see Appendix), which doubtless would last for the construction of one boat—and probably many more—with careful use.

I use only 50-grit paper on both the orbital and the polisher because it clogs less, is easier to clean, and lasts longer than finer paper. This will horrify woodworking purists, who sand and re-sand with successively finer grits. I think that a skiff isn't a piece of furniture and doesn't need to be finished like one. I'll admit a new piece of 50-grit sandpaper will make grooves you can plant potatoes in if you don't move the sander quickly and lightly. But sanding pressure and speed quickly becomes less critical as the paper dulls and loads up a bit.

Buy *closed-faced* paper for the orbital sander; it clogs less and cleans easier than *open-faced* paper. Hardware stores sell it precut in ¼ sheets just for orbitals, or you can quarter full sheets. You can also cut your own discs for the polisher from open-faced, 8½- by 11-inch paper, a cheaper alternative to buying the precut, self-sticking discs, and as a bonus the leftover paper can be used for hand sanding. Jamestown Supply, a wonderful store that specializes in boatbuilders' tools and supplies, sells sandpaper at a good price and is a source for the hard-to-find foam pads for the polisher, the back-up discs that go with them, and feathering disc adhesive for gluing on the paper (see Appendix). Don't neglect to buy one of the gum-rubber sanding-belt cleaners for cleaning the paper on the polisher.

Stationary Power Tools

Table Saw

I rip all the rails and strakes—nearly 200 feet of them for each skiff—with a table saw. If you're skillful and have the nerves and concentration of a jet-fighter pilot you can do it with a Skilsaw, but there are problems. Some of the bottom strakes are plastic, on which it is very difficult to mark a visible line. (A table saw, with its pre-set ripping fence, needs no line.) Also, to allow it to bed firmly along the keel, the center strake must be cut with a vee-shaped groove in its center, perhaps the ultimate Skilsaw challenge.

It's your choice, but a table saw is by far the best tool for ripping. Even a small one, like the 8-inch, 35-pound Makita Model 2708 (about $300) will handle all the ripping, including the plywood. (Delta, a reliable company, offers a similar saw for less than $200 that might do as well, but I've never used one.) The Makita has enough power with its 12-amp motor to rip 2-inch hardwood, and a fence that locks securely and parallel to the blade, the two minimum requirements for any table saw. Small saws in particular benefit from the installation of a thin-rim carbide blade, which increases their effective power 25 percent.

Miter Box

You have to cut lots of tight 30-degree joints between the pieces that make up the strakes and rails. I find it hard to cut these joints accurately with a hand-held saw, so I use a power miter box, which makes the job easy. If the fit isn't perfect on my first try I can shave just a whisker off with this wonderful tool. On the other hand, a poor joint cut by hand must be laboriously planed and filed, or kerfed, a better method in which a saw is run between the faces of the joint until the pieces match perfectly.

I do few other cuts with the power miter box. Nevertheless, it is the perfect complement to the table saw—one rips, the other cuts off—and if you buy one, you might consider buying the other. Together they are among the most commonly used tools for general woodworking. Many good power miter boxes, like the Delta 10-inch Model 34-080 sell for about $200 from Woodworker Supply (see Appendix).

Planer

You can't build the boat without a thickness planer. Before your heart sinks, let me rush on to say you need one for only 20 minutes and you can hire that time at a local woodworking shop. If you want to buy your own planer, you need only the most minimal machine, like the 12-inch Delta bench model (Model 22-540), which sells for less than $400.

In addition to these three stationary tools, I have a band saw, a drill press, and a jointer. All are time-saving conveniences, not necessities, so don't feel like a communist in Eastern Europe if you don't have them. Remember: no one looking at your finished boat will ever know what tools you used to build it.

Epoxy Application Tools

Epoxy is a two-part glue, resin and hardener, that must be mixed in exactly the right amounts to cure properly. You can do this by measuring out the parts in graduated containers, or you can buy pumps that meter out the exact amounts. Pouring into containers is fast for big batches, but small batches—of which you will need many—are hard to measure accurately. A better way to get just a dab or two of epoxy is to squirt the ingredients from syringes epoxy companies sell. These are the smallest, cheapest (less than $10) "pumps" for epoxy. Next in size are plunger pumps that screw into the resin and hardener containers. These are worthless for this project—they can't measure small amounts and are slow to pump large ones. By far the most convenient way to measure epoxy is with a lever-operated pump.

Pumps

Gougeon Brothers, Inc. and System III Resins, the General Motors and Ford of boat-building epoxy companies, both sell lever-operated pumps that are just the right size for projects like this one. One push of the lever and out comes both the epoxy resin and hardener in just the right proportion, a little or a lot, as you wish. You'll like it. If you've been measuring by hand, you'll love it.

Figure 3-2. A System III epoxy pump.

These pumps cost $175 and $200 respectively, so I can easily understand the one-time skiff builder balking at the expense. It may help to think of a lever pump as an investment for a lifetime of projects, including the modification and maintenance of your skiff. Or perhaps you could resell your pump through an ad in *WoodenBoat* or *Boatbuilder* magazines. One project should not reduce its value too much.

In deciding whether to buy a pump, bear in mind that both epoxy resin and hardener are slow-moving, sticky liquids, like honey, and pouring them into and scraping them out of measuring cups is a messy process. The hardener is a mild skin irritant, and its effects are accumulative and irreversible. A man who was going to build an epoxy/plywood sailboat came into my shop looking for epoxy information but didn't take my advice on epoxy pumps. Now if you walk up behind him and just whisper "epoxy," he breaks out in a rash. So if you're the type who can't spread honey on your morning toast without getting it on your knife handle, you better buy a pump.

Containers

You'll need mixing containers. If you eat a lot of spaghetti you're in luck because 4-ounce tomato sauce and mushroom cans are just right for mixing small batches of epoxy putty. You can mix large batches of epoxy or putty in a roller pan, which you can use until it becomes too heavy with cured epoxy. I like the new light throwaway pans; one should last for a whole boat.

Applicators

Once you measure and mix the epoxy you've got to spread it on the boat. I apply epoxy on small areas with brushes. Two sizes work well. I use an acid brush for hard-to-reach areas like the insides of holes or for the edges of the thinnest plywood. These brushes are designed to be disposable, but I keep mine hanging in a sealed container of acetone, which prolongs their life indefinitely. For larger structural joints and for wetting out fiberglass tape in contoured areas, I use a 1½-inch tack brush, a kind of brush made especially for spreading resin. These, too, are throwaways, but I also preserve them in acetone. Buy several of each kind of brush in case you forget to replace them in the acetone.

For the large, open surfaces that make up 95 percent of the boat, I spread epoxy with various sized rollers. Although the epoxy companies sell throwaway foam roller covers, I find them nearly worthless. The epoxy begins to cure inside the foam because the foam traps heat. You know you're in trouble when bits of foam start coming off on the boat while you're fiberglassing the bottom. I want future generations to remember me as the man who discovered The Applicator roller cover (made by Wooster Brush Co.) for spreading epoxy. It is not a regular hardware item and can only be bought at paint and wallpaper stores. Designed specifically for spreading adhesives, it has a short "fur" in which each hair stands separately, effectively dissipating heat. As a bonus, the fur transfers more epoxy from your roller pan to the boat than does the smooth surfaced foam cover. At more than $3, an Applicator is three times as expensive as a foam roller. This cost is slight considering Applicators are easily cleaned and reused. I suggest buying a half dozen, because despite your best cleaning efforts covers will eventually load up with cured epoxy.

Applicator covers are 9 inches long, but buy a best-quality 7-inch roller frame. Also buy a best-quality 3-inch frame and a cheap 3-inch frame, the kind that comes with a shaggy roller cover. Cut 1 inch off the axle of the cheap frame. Now you can carefully

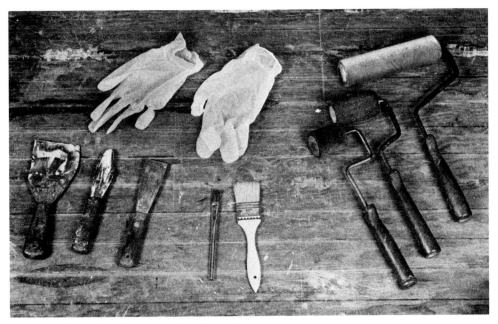

Figure 3-3. Epoxy application tools.

cut 2 inches off a 9-inch cover with a fine toothed saw and cut a second 9-inch cover into thirds. Suit up your frames and you're ready to play the game.

Much of the epoxy that goes into a stitch-and-glue boat is in a thickened form, called putty. Although people have invented special tools to spread it, particularly to make fillets—the radiused strips of putty used to fill the inside corners—I find simple putty knives work best. You'll need two 1-inch knives and one 3-inch knife, all either stiff or flexible, as you prefer. Grind the tip of one of the 1-inch knives to the radius of a nickel for applying small fillets. You can easily clean a putty knife by first letting the epoxy harden, then heating the knife gently with a propane torch and scraping it with another knife.

Epoxy Finishing Tools

Scrapers

All surfaces of the boat are epoxy coated and must be sanded and faired after they cure, both for looks and to make the paint stick. Since the surface of cured epoxy is rougher than that of most coatings—paint, for example—I find sanding is much quicker and more effective if I first level the epoxy with a cabinet scraper (available from Jamestown Supply, see Appendix). This is simply a 3- by 5-inch sheet of tool steel, to which I glue a slotted piece of dowel to make it easier on my hand. The edge of this tool must be kept square and sharp, by filing or by grinding it on a bench grinder.

Cabinet scrapers, effective as they are for levelling the surface of epoxy, are nearly worthless for feathering (tapering out) the edges of fiberglass cloth. You're actually removing a little of the fiberglass along with the epoxy, and glass dulls tool steel very quickly. For years I ground these ugly edges with hand or power sanders, which was not only slow but left a fuzzy fringe of glass. Recently Sandvik of Sweden brought out a wonderful carbide-bladed scraper (available from Woodcraft Supply) that can feather an edge cleanly with one pass. But even carbide edges dull eventually and, being so hard, a diamond stone is required for sharpening. Fortunately these Sandvik blades are reversible, and one will complete a whole skiff without the need for resharpening. Alas, they are only 2 inches wide; what the world needs is a 4-inch-wide carbide scraper. Sandvik, are you listening?

Rasps and Files

Because scrapers can tear out cured drips of epoxy and resin-soaked bits of wood, the epoxy is best ground down roughly before you scrape. The handiest tool for this is the Stanley Surform plane equipped with a 46-grit carbide sanding blade. Most hardware stores carry the tool, but few seem to stock this coarse-grit blade. If you can't find one, it is worth making the effort of having a store order one for you because this tool makes short work of rough-levelling and is easily cleaned with a propane torch and a wire brush.

Coarse files and rasps are the only thing for smoothing tight places and difficult contours. The versatile four-in-hand (shoe rasp) will take the place of several tools with its flat-and-oval shape and choice of coarseness. I carry one at all times in the pocket of my overalls. A 10-inch rattail file is also indispensable for the insides of holes and for grinding small-radius fillets. Bend the tang to a right angle to make a convenient handle.

Do not clean files or rasps (or any other steel cutting tool) with a propane torch; heat will ruin the temper of the steel. If you have the bad luck of plugging a rasp with partially-cured epoxy, you must laboriously poke it out, groove by groove, with the sharp point of a sheetrock screw or the like.

Although you will sand mostly with power sanders, for the places absolutely nothing else will reach you will still need that old hand-sanding standby, the quarter sheet of sandpaper folded into thirds. For greater production in less confined areas, try a small foam sanding block (available in most hardware stores). Since the sandpaper on these blocks is worthless, I peel it off (gently heating it with a torch first) and use feathering disc adhesive to glue on my own 50 grit closed-faced paper.

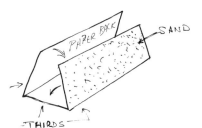

Figure 3-4. The correct way to fold sandpaper for hand use.

Shop Space

There may be parts of the world where a skiff can be built with no shelter, but considering that too little heat, too much heat (especially in the form of direct sunlight), moisture, dust, and even insects are all problems when using epoxy, I think most builders will need some form of shop. A minimum size of 16 by 24 feet—a couple of feet shorter if you choose to build an 18-foot skiff—will provide enough room to cut materials and to turn the hull over during construction. Of course, you can build the skiff in a narrower space, but you'll have to carry the hull outside to turn it over, a job for four strong friends and a couple of six-packs.

If your shop floor is concrete—or if there isn't one—you must build a temporary deck out of 2 × 4s and two sheets of plywood laid end-to-end. It should be smooth enough and of light enough color (you can paint it) to draw on clearly. You will prefabricate many parts of the boat on this deck using screws as clamps, so the plywood can't

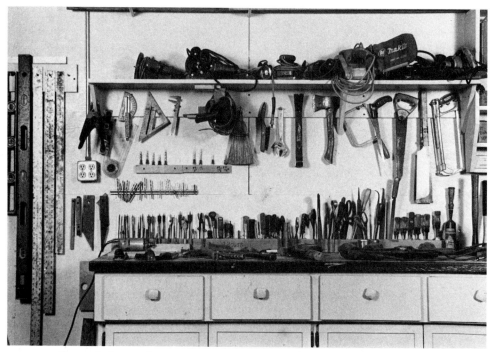

Figure 3-5. A well-found tool bench.

be laid directly onto concrete but must be nailed to framing to give the deck enough thickness to hold the screws. A wooden shop floor is ideal, but if it is dirty or uneven, overlay it with the two 4 × 8 sheets of plywood fastened down without framing.

Tool Bench

Against one wall of your shop you should have a tool bench of about 2 by 8 feet. Notice I said "tool bench", not "work bench"; you will do all your actual cutting and gluing on sawhorses. Get rid of all the tools you use to repair the family car and lay out or hang up only the tools you need for skiff construction. Maybe the power tools can go on a shelf over or under the bench. Once you find a home for each tool, make sure it gets back there every time you use it.

Sawhorses

Sawhorses are like electric drills: you can hardly have enough of them. With five pairs, you can spread out the four side panels for the boat, epoxy them, let them cure for 24 hours, then sand them, and still have a pair of horses to continue work on other parts of the skiff. If five pairs seem extravagant, settle for two and think up some temporary supports for the side panels. One of your pairs should be set up more or less permanently near your tool bench, with a shelf under the nearer horse for your Skilsaw.

If you don't already own sawhorses, build a few pairs. Do you know that there are 15 ways to build sawhorses? Fourteen are wrong; the fifteenth is shown in Figure 3-12. These horses are lightweight, stackable, and designed to last many years. If you're naughty and saw a top in two by mistake, you can replace it easily.

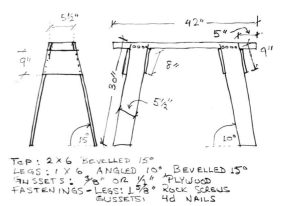

Top: 2×6 Bevelled 15°
Legs: 1×6 Angled 10°, Bevelled 15°
Gussets: 3/8" or 1/2" Plywood
Fastenings—Legs: 1 5/8" Rock Screws
Gussets: 4d Nails

Figure 3-6. How to build a sawhorse—way 15.

Lighting

You can't build a good skiff without good lighting. Strong overhead lighting coming from several sources to eliminate shadows is best. If your garage is lit by a single dingy light bulb, try rigging a string of temporary lights on #12 Romex (the basic wire used in house construction). Hardware stores sell handy light sockets developed for the construction trades that simply screw onto and penetrate the Romex. You should also have a spotlight on a moveable stand you can shine on your work at different angles to show up imperfections.

The imperfections in your epoxy coating may be more than merely cosmetic. (Here I am talking about wood coated with epoxy alone, not wood covered with fiberglass and epoxy.) To be wholly effective, epoxy must provide a seamless waterproof barrier. Any breach in the surface, no matter how tiny, will let in moisture that can swell the wood and crack the finish; Murphy could have had epoxy boats in mind when he wrote his famous law. On the other hand, it is hard to cover wood with epoxy and fiberglass and not seal it, a smooth finish being mostly a matter of appearance. But if looks are important—and I think they should be—let me warn you that it can be a rude shock when you pull your skiff out into the daylight for the first time and see the glitches that got by you. So the best of shop lighting is none too good.

Heat

Your work area must be warm. One of the most unfortunate things said about epoxy—and said often—is that it works well in cold conditions. Epoxy will indeed cure in temperatures down to freezing but it loses strength when it cures in cold conditions, although probably not enough to cause a disaster. But epoxy applied below 50 degrees will take literally days to cure sufficiently to sand properly. While slow curing is merely an inconvenience, the most serious consequence of using epoxy at low temperatures is that it doesn't penetrate the wood properly. I know a man who fiberglassed his skiff in spring weather of less than 50 degrees only to have the whole layer of glass separate and peel off shortly after launching.

How warm is "warm"? Let's say, arbitrarily, 60 degrees or above when you're actually spreading epoxy on the boat. I like to keep my shop close to 70 degrees during the day and not less than 50 at night so that I can sand epoxy efficiently the morning after I spread it. If you can't maintain these temperatures, the best compromise is to keep the containers of epoxy and hardener warm at all times. Bring them to a warm place at night or insulate and provide heat for them in your shop. I spread a sleeping bag over my pumps and put a 15-watt light bulb under it. I have heard that an inverted Styrofoam icebox makes a handy insulator.

Manuals for epoxy use suggest heat lamps, heat guns, or space heaters to provide direct heat on your work. They also suggest putting boat parts under plastic tents with heat sources underneath. It seems to me this advice applies more to fixing broken teacups than to curing 20-foot-long sections of a Tolman Skiff. I would make an exception for a couple of critical structural joints that are assembled on the floor. If your floor is cold, these joints will benefit from a shot of heat from a heat lamp or hair drier. In general, the best strategy is to try to get the whole shop warm enough.

Clearly, using epoxy in cool conditions requires common sense—and even ingenuity. Since epoxy generates its own heat, the bigger the batch and the longer you mix it, the better. (Warning! Work up to using big batches slowly. Too big a batch will fire off in the pot—it can literally burst into flame.) Likewise, the thicker you spread it, layer on layer, the better. Spread epoxy early in the day to give it the benefit of warmer daytime shop temperatures. Place coated items close to the ceiling—perhaps on temporary racks or hung in loops of line. Plan your work so as to postpone sanding as long as possible —but not scraping, which is done best when the epoxy is soft. Motto: scrape early, sand late. And remember: a cure that starts well ends well. Didn't Shakespeare say something like that?

Dedicate one area of your tool bench for your epoxy and the various tool, rags, mixing containers, and fillers you use with it, then get in the habit of putting all these things back there after you use them. This sure beats finding that your roller pan has dripped epoxy onto the handle of your drill. Even better than a place on your tool bench for all this glue stuff is a table of, say, 32 by 48 inches that can be moved close to the work

Figure 3-7. A Cadillac of a glue cart.

you're doing. Better still is a glue cart on wheels, an idea I got from the Gougeon Brothers. Mine has storage underneath for less frequently used items like acetone (for cleaning) and extra epoxy.

Finally, make sure your shop has neither a coffee pot nor a comfortable place to sit. These will only increase the natural attraction boatshops have for spectators, who are ever full of bad advice. (Let's hope you don't need any advice, good or bad.) But don't be too inhospitable—there will be a couple of times during this project when an extra hand will be a great help.

4 | Choosing Materials

If you have assembled your tools and have come up with shop space, it's time to think about materials. This chapter tells you about all the materials you'll need to build the skiff, except for the epoxy and fiberglass, which is such a big subject I've given it Chapter 5 by itself. Before you actually buy your materials, I suggest you read both Chapters 4 and 5. In both, the amounts and sizes of materials given are for building a 20-foot skiff with the two most popular options—lockers at the bow and stern. Materials for such add-ons as steering consoles and storage boxes are listed, along with how to build them, in Chapter 15. There is certain other lumber you will need for a building jig and a couple of other items not part of the finished boat. I list this lumber as you actually need it during the building process.

After you read this chapter and price materials, you may go into shock when you add up the bill. All I can say is my recommendations for materials are based on having built skiffs out of poorer materials—non-marine-grade plywood, for example—which I didn't think were satisfactory. And if it will make you feel better, I can tell you that you could easily spend much more if you bought clear framing lumber or super-expensive foreign-made marine plywood. It may help to think of the extra dollars spent for better materials as protecting your investment. If you build out of good materials and with care, I believe there is no practical limit to the lifespan of your skiff. If you build out of materials intended for houses, not boats, who knows how long it will last? A crude expression sums it up: shit in, shit out.

Planking

The skin of a Tolman Skiff, referred to in boatbuilding terms as *planking,* is ⅜-inch plywood on the sides of the boat and ½-inch on the bottom. I use fir plywood, although it is sometimes criticized by other boatbuilders for two reasons.

First, since fir is a wood whose grain is alternately soft and hard, it sands unevenly and the grain of the wood tends to show through the paint finish. Epoxy and fiberglass correct this. Fiberglassed surfaces show no wood grain and non-fiberglassed surfaces can be built up with extra epoxy and sanded perfectly smooth. Frankly, I don't mind seeing a little wood grain.

The second criticism is more serious. The surface of fir plywood tends to *check*, that is, to develop fine cracks, due to the release of tension built in during manufacture. Checking lets in moisture which eventually will cause the paint finish to peel and, in extreme cases, can even destroy the epoxy beneath it. At this stage rot can occur under some conditions. That fir plywood checks is an argument for using foreign-made, hardwood marine plywood instead, which stands up better but is around double the price of even the best grade of fir plywood. I believe it is not only better but cheaper as well to eliminate the checking in the fir ply by covering it with fiberglass. More about this in the next chapter.

I use only *marine-grade* plywood. Marine-grade is the aristocrat of the many grades of fir plywood and relatively expensive. It is graded AA or AB, which means both sides of the sheet, or faces, have no unpatched defects and are sanded smooth. (For practical purposes A and B faces are the same; the difference lies only in the number and kinds of patches.)

Some boatbuilders argue that since epoxy and fiberglass are so wonderful, you can use non-marine-grade, saving from one half to two thirds on the plywood cost (the relative prices of the two grades depends on the thickness of the sheets). The grade they usually suggest is AC exterior, abbreviated ACX. This designation means the plywood has one face that has no unpatched defects and is sanded smooth—the A side—and one that can have knotholes and other unpatched defects—the C side. Patch the knotholes with epoxy putty, these builders tell us, and save hundreds of dollars.

Yes, but . . . . And there are several big ones. To start with, the interior layers of ACX need only to be of C quality. That means knotholes and cracks in these layers form voids in the interior of the sheet. Suppose your boat goes aground on a rock that punches the outer layer of plywood into a void. Or you drop your anchor onto the bottom of your boat and it makes a hole. In either case water enters the plywood, running who knows where, and I don't know how to tell you how to get it out.

This isn't all the bad news about ACX. Three-eighths-inch plywood, the thickness used for the sides of a Tolman Skiff, has such a thin veneer of wood on its A face that it is very easily shattered when you saw or plane it. This delicate layer is also prone to swelling and bubbling if the slightest amount of moisture gets into the panel. Theoretically none should if the panel is well-sealed with epoxy, but what if the surface checks? You could cover it with fiberglass cloth, but there goes most of your cost savings.

Since the A veneer of ⅜-inch ACX is thin, the middle layer—there is only one—is correspondingly thick. This is not in itself bad, but I have often seen pulpy or even rotten wood in this core. I hear rumors that this layer need not even be fir but can be made of softer, weaker species of wood. Such a panel must be far less strong. Is it strong enough? I don't know.

Perhaps you're beginning to see why I don't let anything but marine plywood through the door of my shop. Graded only AA or AB, marine ply is much easier to seal up effectively with epoxy because its surfaces are smooth to start with. But the most important aspect of marine ply is that all the interior layers are of A or B quality as well, so there are no interior voids. Every layer, and typically there are more of them than in ACX, is of equal thickness and of good quality.

Figure 4-1. Typical voids in exterior-grade plywood.

As a fringe benefit marine ply—and only marine—comes in lengths longer than 8 feet. Although you can join panels end-to-end by a process known as scarfing—and indeed you'll have to do this to build a Tolman Skiff— you may as well start out with 10- and 12-foot panels and save yourself a lot of work.

As a final consideration, suppose you take up golf and sell your skiff. If you are honest (I hope you would be) and declare that it is made of ACX plywood, who will buy it? Not the customers who buy my skiffs, certainly. People are apt to be mistrustful of plywood as a boatbuilding material, associating it with the bad old days before epoxy and fiberglass when plywood boats were known as rotters. You may as well at least give them the reassurance your skiff is made from marine ply, a material intended specifically for boats.

You will need the following plywood:

4 sheets	4×8 feet $\times \frac{1}{4}$ inch
1 "	4×8 feet $\times \frac{3}{8}$ inch
2 "	4×10 feet $\times \frac{3}{8}$ inch
2 "	4×12 feet $\times \frac{3}{8}$ inch
1 "	4×8 feet $\times \frac{1}{2}$ inch
2 "	4×12 feet $\times \frac{1}{2}$ inch

Framing

Although I classify the Tolman Skiff as a stitch-and-glue skiff, it does have some framing. Only the bowstem functions like the framing in a conventionally built boat by joining the two side panels; the rest of the framing supports the panels but doesn't join them together—more what you might expect in a typical stitch-and-glue boat. The names and locations of the various framing members are shown in Figure 4-2. Most of the framing has names you'd expect, but I'd like to direct your attention to the two members toward the stern that run up the side panels like ribs. I call them *rear framing* for lack of a better name.

I make all the framing out of Douglas fir. You can't beat fir: it's strong, is easily worked with tools, and glues well. Perhaps surprisingly, good fir is cheap and readily available—at least the kind I use. The lumber traditionally associated with boatbuilding is *clear*, meaning free of knots. Clear fir costs around $3.50 per board foot. Instead I buy a grade called *select structural*, which costs about 75 cents per board foot. Much select structural lumber is clear. The rest has only small knots that are oriented across the thickness of the plank and weaken it very little. Select structural lumber is used, among other places, in the house-building industry for making trusses. Since most ranch-style houses use roof trusses, you can see there must be a lot of this lumber available around the country. If your local lumber company operates a truss factory, as mine does, they should be glad to sell you what you need.

It is also possible to frame your skiff out of regular construction-grade lumber found in most lumber yards, but beware of lumber marked hem-fir because most of it seems to be hemlock, not Douglas fir. Hemlock is interchangeable with fir for most elements of house construction, but it is a poor boatbuilding wood because it is too brittle. So use construction-grade lumber only if you can find Douglas fir (identified by its pinkish color) of good quality, that is, straight and reasonably knot-free. Some lumber

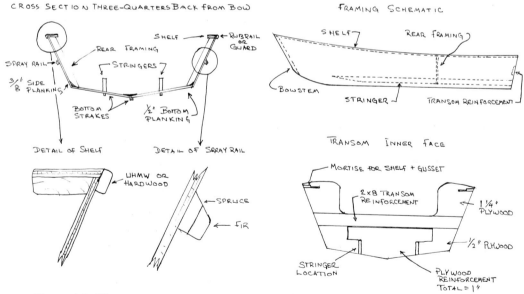

Figure 4-2. The parts of a Tolman Skiff.

A SKIFF FOR ALL SEASONS

companies will let you pick through their stacks, charging a little extra for the privilege. Some won't.

If you can't come up with Douglas fir, I can only suggest substituting a wood close in weight and structural properties. Some of the Philippine mahoganies (there are many kinds) come close. Some other domestic softwoods have proved themselves for boat framing—Alaska yellow cedar, larch, and Sitka spruce among them. If you use spruce, be sure it is Sitka spruce and not the much weaker white spruce, common in the lumber yards of the northern United States.

For framing you will need the following:

4 pieces 2 x 8 inches x 20 feet

(The lengths of the planks are a little greater than you'll actually need in your skiff. This lets you eliminate the worst defects and match the best piece of lumber for each piece of framing. This extra lumber is well worth the few extra dollars.)

Figure 4-3. Douglas fir framing lumber.

Spray Rails

The rails that run outside the hull along the center of the side panels not only block spray but stiffen the panels, taking the place of the ribs found in conventional wooden skiffs. These rails are laminated from two layers of 1-inch softwood. They are 19 feet long and both layers can be gotten out of a 1 × 4. However, you will be ripping some of your 2 × 8 to make the stringers, and if you are lucky enough to have purchased good framing lumber, the pieces ripped off can be resawn to make up the outer, smaller lamination. So before you buy the stock for spray rails, look these rippings over and decide whether they are sufficiently knot-free to use. You will need a minimum of 12 feet of stock strong enough to bend around the front part of the boat without breaking. The rest of the run can be put on in a couple of short pieces. This means given the amount of stock you have, you can saw out two large knots per rail if you need to.

I use local spruce for spray rails, knots and all. And by the way, you can afford more knots in the inner layer; it's the outer lamination that gives the rail its strength. Pine graded #3 common, or any other locally available softwood, would do as well as spruce.

If your local wood seems excessively knotty, perhaps you'll want to buy extra stock in the form of wider boards.

For the inner lamination you'll need:

2 pieces 1 x 4 inch x 14 feet

For the outer lamination you'll need:

2 pieces 1 x 3 inch x 14 feet

Strakes

In this category I lump the strakes that protect the gunwales, called rubrails or guards, with the three that run along the bottom of the boat (see Figure 4-2). The middle one of these runs continuously from the stern to the top of the stem and protects the bow. On my first skiffs I used hardwood for all the strakes, but the one running along the keel would soon be crushed and shredded from running the skiffs on the beach. To correct that I tried using ironbark, a very dense, tough species of eucalyptus used on the West Coast on commercial fishing boats. Then a few years ago I noticed plastic was replacing ironbark for guards on commercial boats.

Plastic Rails

I found out that a couple of different kinds of plastic were being used, but the best—and by far the most expensive—was ultra high molecular weight polyethylene, abbreviated UHMW. UHMW is not only abrasion resistant, outwearing steel in certain applications, but is able to absorb high impact. As a bonus it is very slippery; local dog mushers are using it on their sled runners. I tried it for protection on the keels of my skiffs, and it was a great success.

Since UHMW is so expensive—more than $13 per board foot—I leave it up to you whether you want to make only the bottom strakes out of it, or whether you want to make the rubrails out of it as well. It is sold by plastics distributors (see "Plastic—Sheets" in the yellow pages of your phone book) in 4 × 10-foot × ¾-inch sheets and comes in black or white. Perhaps these plastics distributors won't want to sell less than a whole sheet. If so, ask them to whom they sell these sheets and then contact these business and ask whether they will sell you what you need. In the Seattle area Wesbrook Marine (see appendix) will sell any amount and will even cut it exactly to your specifications. (See Chapter 12 for bottom strake dimensions.)

For bottom strakes you'll need:

1 piece 4 inches x 10 feet x ¾ inch

For UHMW rubrails you'll need:

1 piece 8 inches x 10 feet x ¾ inch

Wouldn't you know? The rubrails for a 20-foot skiff are a bit over 21 feet long, so it's necessary to buy material for five lengths of rail. It probably would stretch any company's good will too far to ask them to sell you less than a whole 10-foot length. Never mind. It's handy stuff, and I'll give you some suggestions for uses for some of the left-over.

Hardwood Rails

If you choose hardwood rubrails, I suggest oak or any other similar, rot-resistant hardwood. I like apitong, a form of Philippine mahogany with the properties of oak. It machines and glues well and is a handsome dark red if left natural and finished off with a mixture of pine tar and linseed oil. It is widely available, on the West Coast at least, for about $2 per board foot.

If you buy the following amount, you will have enough left over for a coaming cap for the drywell:

1 piece 2 x 6 inch x 12 feet

Fastenings

You could well ask what the function of fastenings is in a boat that is essentially held together by glue and fiberglass. The primary function of many fastenings is temporary, holding elements together until the glue sets. They then may or may not be removed, depending upon where they are located. If they are not removed, they operate in a belt-and-suspenders fashion, adding to the strength of the glue joint. I have done destructive testing of various parts of the boat and have concluded some joints benefit greatly from additional mechanical fastenings. Consider a simple butt joint between two pieces of plywood (Figure 4-4). If you have to put fasteners in anyway, why not leave them in? Sometimes, of course, they can't stay in because they are in the way of later cutting or fairing.

Figure 4-4. Box nails hold a simple butt joint until the glue sets.

Screws

I believe the most critical joint in the boat is that between the stringers and the bottom panels. The bottom of a planing-hull boat takes a tremendous beating as it leaves and re-enters the water during rough sea conditions, which is why I specify that the bottom be fastened with stainless screws as well as glue. Screws hold much better than nails in this situation, where force is being exerted on the fastening end-ways, and stainless screws are much less brittle than the sheetrock screws I specify for less critical joints.

A second, more obvious place for stainless screws is in the plastic bottom strakes where the screw heads will be exposed. Here again the toughness of the fastenings is important, so even if you install hardwood rubrails whose fastenings will be countersunk and filled, use stainless screws. Of course, all hardware should be mounted with stainless screws (with the exception of oarlock sockets, which need bronze screws).

For all other places that I call for screws, the cheap, easily-driven sheetrock screw will do fine. Galvanized sheetrock screws are now available for pennies more than the original black variety. If you damage the epoxy coating over the screw head and water gets to it, galvanizing will give it protection. But this is a small point, so if your store doesn't have the galvanized variety the old kind are fine.

Speaking of screws, the familiar wood screw, with its slotted head and threads that stop part way up the shank, is obsolete. Although this kind of screw is still being sold, it is fast being replaced by screws like the sheetrock screw with Phillips heads and fully threaded shanks. These are called *tapping* screws, and by all means specify tapping screws when you buy your stainless fastenings. You then can drive all the screws used in the skiff with the same #2 Phillips screwdriver bit in your electric drill.

Nails

I would judge that over half the fastenings I call for in the skiff are ordinary galvanized box nails. (A box nail, by the way, is a nail made from thinner wire than a so-called common nail.) Please don't substitute screws for nails. I use nails in situations where the loading on them is in shear, meaning at right angles to the shank. A nail used thus is perhaps a little stronger than a brittle sheetrock screw, while a stainless screw is unnecessarily expensive and slow to drive compared to a nail. There are some other reasons for nails I'll point out when the actual construction begins.

Unless—and perhaps even if—you have an excellent chandlery catering to the needs of a commercial fishing fleet, the best place to buy stainless fastenings is Jamestown Supply (see Appendix). They're amazingly cheap and have a wonderful selection. If you are ordering by phone or mail, make doubly certain you include all the information about the fastening: type of metal, numbered size, length, head style (meaning flathead, panhead, etc.), and head shape (meaning Phillips or slotted). Take it from your Old Dad, it's easy to order the wrong thing.

You will need the following fastenings:

Stainless flathead Phillips tapping screws:
    100 each   #6 × ⅜ inch
    100 "   #8 × 1¼ inch
    100 "   #8 × 1½ inch
    100 "   #10 × 2 inch

Stainless panhead Phillips tapping screws:
    100 each   #8 × ¼ inch

Bronze flathead Phillips wood screws (they don't make bronze tapping screws):
    14 each   #8 × 1 inch

Sheetrock screws (numbered size is determined by length):
    ½ pound   1 inch
    1   "   1¼ inch
    1   "   1⅝ inch
    ½   "   2 inch
    ½   "   2½ inch

Galvanized box nails:
    1½ pounds 3d
    ½   "   4d
    1   "   6d
    ½   "   8d

Hardware

My personal taste is for minimal hardware on a skiff: less to snag on, to break, to corrode. Less to paint around. And I like the clean look. But if you want to encrust your boat with lots of cleats and chocks, that's up to you. As a substitute for cleats I use holes.

Near the point of the bow I drill two holes (Figure 4-5) through which I lead the painter around the bowstem—about as

Figure 4-5. Bow holes. The upper pair is for the painter. The lower pair, sealed with tubing, is for a towline or the trailer connection.

secure a setup as you can get. Further down the bowstem are a second pair of holes for attaching a towline. This is also the right place to attach your boat trailer's winch cable. Don't even consider the old-fashioned galvanized eye bolt, even if it is reinforced with a so-called shoulder. Eye bolts bend when they come up against docks or boat trailers, enlarging the hole drilled for them in the bowstem. I've seen more than a few bowstems rotted because of this.

To seal off the lower pair of holes from water entering the boat, I borrowed a neat idea from George Hamm, my boatbuilding advisor from early days. I install two copper pipe elbows and a short piece of connecting tubing to make a U-shaped tube encircling the bowstem (Figure 4-5). For this bow pipe, as I call it, you'll need:

- $12\frac{3}{4}$ inches of $1\frac{1}{4}$-inch copper tubing

- 2 copper street 90s, $1\frac{1}{4}$ inch

Street 90 is plumbers lingo for an elbow. I'll explain installation at the appropriate time.

Instead of installing cleats, I drill holes in the shelf (as I call the gunwale structure of my skiffs) for securing fenders and side and stern tie-up lines. For heavy-duty towing jobs, like towing skiers or dead-in-the-water boats, I loop a line through the two drain holes in the drywell.

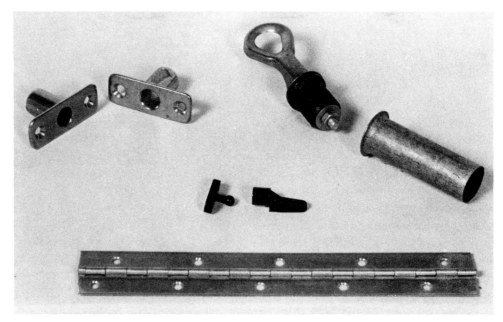

Figure 4-6. A Snap-Tite drain plug and brass tube, stainless steel piano hinge, a Perko door catch, and a pair of "regular" oarlock sockets.

A SKIFF FOR ALL SEASONS

If you build a bulkhead under the drywell at the stern (see Chapter 2 for design options), you'll need an 8-inch deck plate and, for better access, two 6-inchers, one at either side. I like the pop-out type made by Beckson (available from Jamestown Supply). If your rubrails are UHMW, you'll probably want the deck plates black to match.

The installation of the bulkhead also requires 15 inches of 1-inch-ID copper tube to extend the drain through to the transom. Bulkhead or not you'll need a Snap-Tite drain plug and the 1-inch-OD brass tube that goes with it (also available from Jamestown Supply).

If you opt for a thwart/storage box (see Chapter 2), buy a 6-foot stick of 1½-inch stainless steel piano hinge (screws have already been figured in the fastening list). To prevent the lid from opening too far I attach about 18 inches of light galvanized chain known in the fishing industry as brailer chain; any light galvanized or brass chain will do. The lid can be secured with nifty little plastic door catches made by Perko (N559 LP—sold in pairs).

If you want oarlocks, and most people do, bronze are the only kind worth considering. The galvanized kind won't stand up under the force developed by the 10-foot oars you'll need. Get 2¼-inch rings or horns, as you prefer, and *regular* sockets (as distinct from *side plate* or *angle plate*) to match the oarlocks (Jamestown Supply).

If you decide on the bow locker, you will have enough piano hinge remaining from what you used to make the center thwart cover. The only other items you'll need are a second pair of Perko door catches and, if you want to lock the locker, a small, marine-grade hasp.

Bedding Compound

The strakes are all bedded in and sealed around the edges with bedding compound, not epoxy; epoxy doesn't have enough flexibility. I use black Sikaflex 241, a polyurethane marine caulking compound. ("marine" means it is rated for use below the waterline.) I like this brand much better than the familiar 3M 5200 because it sets up overnight instead of taking the week that 5200 requires. Also, because Sikaflex isn't quite as strong, you have a better chance of removing a damaged strake without tearing the boat apart. One tube is probably enough if you don't clip off too much of the end of the spout.

All hardware above the waterline should be bedded in and sealed with clear silicone caulk. Not only is silicone easy to apply and clean up, but removing the hardware later if need be is much easier than with, say, polyurethane, which might tear up your boat. One tube will easily do a skiff.

The drain tube is the only piece of hardware below the waterline, and silicone caulk is not rated for this application. Nor will polyurethane work because it seems to react with the copper and brass. I hate telling you you've got to buy a $7 tube of special caulk just for the one squirt necessary to seal the drain, but it's the best solution I've come up with to prevent leaking drain tubes. After rejecting a couple of different products I'm now using one called Lexel, but it's too early to tell whether it's the final solution. If any of you builders come up with the perfect caulk for this application, I'd like to hear from you.

Paint

You must paint your skiff. Epoxy withstands attack by just about anything you can think of except sunlight. After all my lecturing on using first rate materials for building your skiff, it may surprise you to hear me say that whatever kind of paint you choose is fine by me. Any paint, even a thin coat, lasts a long time over epoxy. Here's why. Moisture goes through the paint but will not affect the epoxy, which can't absorb it. Epoxy will not change dimension, which would break the bond of the paint and cause it to peel. But having said this, I've got to admit more and better paint will last longer.

I paint my skiffs with an ordinary general-purpose high-gloss enamel paint sold at my local hardware store. In fine print on the back of the can it says, in addition to its being suitable for painting kitchen sinks, etc., "for marine use." This means the paint has a higher-than-ordinary percentage of solids, which are what remains on your boat after the paint dies. I figure not having a picture of a boat on the front of the can makes it cost a third less. I can expect about three seasons out of a paint job—but probably I would get less if I lived in Florida instead of Alaska.

So use what paint you like. Two-part epoxies and linear polyurethanes, while expensive, are wonderfully durable, but only you can decide if they're worth it. I will say they're not worth using unless your whole skiff is fiberglassed. These extremely hard paints are also brittle and perform much better over hard substrata, such as fiberglass. And a word of caution about any paint: try it on a sample of epoxied wood first. Some paints react with recently cured epoxy. Even though the epoxy is hard, even sandable, a small amount of uncombined molecules remains, which can combine with certain paints and prevent them from drying.

One gallon of primer and two of paint are enough to paint a skiff with one and two coats, respectively. Primer isn't absolutely necessary, but it's just one more layer of protection. I use Petit Fiberglass Undercoater; I'm sure lots of other primers are as good. If you want to paint the shelf and spray rails a contrasting color, as you'll notice so many skiff owners do, one quart of paint is enough. I'll make some suggestions in Chapter 14 on how to go about painting your skiff.

5 | Epoxy and Fiberglass

Epoxy and fiberglass are a large part of a stitch-and-glue skiff. Epoxy is used as a glue to structurally attach wood to wood, as a sealer to waterproof wood surfaces, with fillers to make putty, and as a bonding agent to attach fiberglass cloth to the wood. The fiberglass is used to reinforce wood surfaces and to join the wood structurally as well. When you build a Tolman Skiff, you will spend at least as much time spreading epoxy and applying fiberglass as you will cutting and fitting wood. You should recognize that using epoxy and fiberglass well takes at least as much skill as woodworking.

Epoxy As a Glue

Epoxy is different from other glues in an important respect: when it hardens it doesn't shrink. For example, if you fill a gap between two pieces of wood with epoxy and let it cure, the gap remains full. Try this with yellow carpenter's glue and the gap returns as the glue dries and shrinks away. Consequently, wood glued with epoxy doesn't need to be closely fitted or tightly clamped. You don't need to make full contact between the pieces you want to join as long as the space between them is

Figure 5-1. Wood joint filled with epoxy putty. Note fillet added to inside of joint.

Figure 5-2. Step 1: coat glue surfaces with unthickened epoxy until saturated.

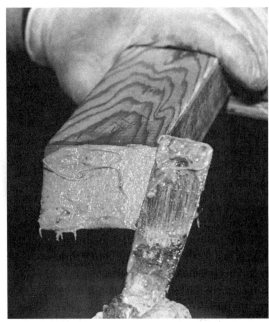

Figure 5-3. Step 2: add thickened epoxy to fill the gaps.

completely filled with epoxy. In fact, if after the epoxy cures you see that there are voids in the joint you have made, because the epoxy has soaked in or run out, you can refill the voids with epoxy without losing any strength in the joint.

You're getting off easy. Compare using epoxy to using resorcinol, a waterproof glue widely used for boatbuilding before epoxy came along. To use resorcinol right you are supposed to fit the surfaces to be glued to a tolerance of $\frac{1}{100}$ inch and clamp them together with 100 pounds of pressure. I can't even see $\frac{1}{100}$ inch any more let alone fit wood that tightly.

But don't be misled: epoxy has to be used right to work right. One misleading statement that has been made many times about epoxy is that it has "gap-filling properties." Not by itself it doesn't. Put plain epoxy into a glue joint and it will tend to soak in or run out. To give it the thickness it needs to stay in a loose joint you must mix it with *microfibers*, a structural filler. But that creates a different problem: epoxy thickened with microfibers won't penetrate the wood deep enough to make a strong joint. The solution is to *always* coat both glue surfaces with unthickened epoxy until they will absorb no more before you add epoxy thickened with fibers to fill any gaps in the joint. Gluing with epoxy should always be a two-part process: first you saturate and then you fill. I'll repeat this so often as we go along, you'll want to set it to music.

A second way to go wrong gluing with epoxy is to glue to cured epoxy that hasn't been sanded. The epoxy makers tell us that new epoxy will only bond chemically to old epoxy if the old epoxy is less than 24 hours old. After that the bond is mechanical only,

A SKIFF FOR ALL SEASONS

and the surface of the old epoxy must be well roughed up with coarse sandpaper for the new epoxy to get a grip. The roughened surface then must be thoroughly and carefully cleaned, not merely by brushing but with a rag dampened with water to which ammonia has been added. As if this isn't enough, you've then got to make sure the surface is completely dry because uncured epoxy hates dampness.

Sealing Wood

All the wood in a Tolman Skiff is completely sealed with epoxy, a process called *epoxy saturation*. For the seal to work there must be two coats of epoxy applied to 100 percent of the surface of the skiff—under the shelves, in the lockers, everywhere. No area is any less important than any other area. Wood is like a sponge and will absorb moisture even if water isn't present on its surface; in other words, it will absorb even dampness from the air. But when the wood is coated with epoxy, which, unlike paint, is nonporous, no moisture in any form, liquid or vapor, can enter the wood.

Air, of course, can't penetrate the seal either, and although epoxy saturation has been used successfully for twenty years or so, there are still boat designers and builders who say wood fully coated with epoxy will rot because it can't breathe. Here are the facts. Rot is caused by fungi that feed on the wood. Rot fungi spores are certain to be present in the wood, but in addition to wood for food, they need a temperature above about 42 degrees, moisture, and oxygen to thrive. You can't refrigerate your skiff, but you can coat it with epoxy to keep water and air away from the spores. If you can keep the epoxy seal intact—that is, not let the wood breathe—your skiff can't rot.

Epoxy Putty

You'll use a wheelbarrow load of putty to build a Tolman Skiff. The biggest volume of this putty is used to make the large fillets along the keel and chine joints, and for smaller fillets along most of the other plywood-to-plywood joints. Filling voids and imperfections in the wood is another important use. Before you seal wood with epoxy, you must fill absolutely every knothole and hairline crack no matter how small—even around the footballs in the plywood (as the patches are descriptively called). You must pay special attention to endgrain, which for plywood means all edges. By carefully filling all these areas first, you can then seal the wood with two coats of epoxy. If you don't fill with putty, several coats may not be enough. So much for epoxy's gap-filling properties.

Putty is made by adding various powdered fillers to the epoxy. These can be used singly or together, and I change the recipe according to where I'm going to use the putty. In addition to microfibers, which thicken the epoxy for structural gluing, I use microballoons and microspheres. Both are powders consisting of tiny hollow balls, balloons being plastic and spheres glass. Both weaken the epoxy and should not be used for structural gluing. And both make a porous putty that isn't waterproof unless it's coated with epoxy after it's applied. I use wood flour, which is simply extremely fine sawdust, for blending with the microballoons in situations where I need a high-strength fillet.

The last additive I use is a silica thickener, Cab-O-Sil, which looks like very fine soap flakes. A little of this amazing stuff thickens epoxy without increasing its volume or affecting its strength or waterproofness. Cab-O-Sil can be added to epoxy to prevent drips or sagging on vertical surfaces, or mixed with putty made from other fillers to get just the right consistency.

You will need the following amounts of fillers:

- 1 pound microfibers

- 1 pound microballoons

- 1 pound microspheres

- 1 pound wood flour

- 1 pound Cab-O-Sil

Figure 5-4. Making epoxy putty.

Bonding Fiberglass

A large part of the surface of a Tolman Skiff is not only sealed with epoxy but covered with fiberglass cloth bonded with epoxy. (How much of the skiff to cover is detailed later in this chapter.) Although I specify epoxy for bonding the cloth, it is possible to apply fiberglass with so-called fiberglass resin, more accurately called polyester resin, which costs about one third as much as epoxy. I have one word to say: don't. I'd leave it at that except there are still books and articles written and boat plans sold that approve of using polyester resin on plywood boats.

Polyester resin is a great product in its place, which is in fiberglasss boats, but it is not at all suitable for use with wood. Polyester *cures*, meaning it changes chemically, but like paint, it also *dries*, losing about seven percent to evaporation. So, like paint, polyester is porous. When it is used on a wooden boat, moisture enters, the wood swells, and the bond between the wood and the fiberglass, not very strong to begin with, breaks. Water then accumulates between the glass and the wood, and you have a boat that is heavy today and rotten tomorrow.

You can cover a wooden boat successfully with glass and polyester resin, but only if you use lots of both. A thick layer reduces the chance of this relatively brittle resin of shattering under impact and slows moisture absorption, but then you are really building two boats, one hull around another. This is expensive, costing more than a thin layer of fiberglass and epoxy. It is also heavy, and if there's one thing you don't need in a boat that planes, it's extra weight.

Epoxy does what polyester promises: it bonds and seals. When it cures, almost nothing evaporates. The result is a material that is virtually non-porous and moisture proof. Epoxy is also much more flexible than polyester. Tests have shown that it can stand much greater impact before cracking enough to let water through. And of course the strength of the epoxy bond is legendary—if you tear the glass off the bottom of your skiff, the wood will come with it.

For all uses—glue, filler, and sealer—construction of the 20-foot Tolman Skiff described in this book requires:

> 10 gallons of epoxy (total combined volume of epoxy and
> hardener)

Choosing An Epoxy

Epoxy resin and the hardener that goes with it aren't single chemical compounds but are mixtures blended to suit their intended use. For this project by all means choose a boatbuilder's epoxy. You can build a good skiff with any of several different brands, but two stand out because they are both easier to use and cheaper than the rest. They are Gougeon Brothers (usually known as WEST System) and System Three—the General Motors and Ford of boatbuilder's epoxies. These brands are especially convenient because each also offers a full product line of fillers, fiberglass, pumps, and other tools you'll need (see Appendix for addresses), and I suggest you choose one or the other. I've built lots of skiffs with each brand, and I'll tell you how they are different and why I'm a Ford man.

Mix

WEST System is mixed at a ratio of five parts resin to one part hardener, whereas System Three is mixed two to one. This makes no difference if you have an epoxy metering pump, but if you are mixing by hand, the two-to-one mix is easier, especially when mixing small batches. System Three makes it even easier by being a formula that works even if you miss the measurements by a small amount.

Epoxy Metering Pumps

Both systems offer lever pumps, as recommended in Chapter 3. The metering pump from System Three, though slightly more expensive, seems to be more trouble free than the one made by the Gougeon Brothers. Because of the differences in mixing ratios, the System Three pump will not work with WEST System epoxy (and vice versa).

Moisture Sensitivity

Moisture is the enemy of curing epoxy and can cause it to turn milky or even not to cure properly. The makers of System Three claim their epoxy is blended to be less sensitive to high humidity than that of the competition. I build boats where this isn't a problem, but for those of you where it could be, this should be consideration.

Price

As I write this, System Three epoxy is cheaper, and they pay the shipping. On the amount needed to build a skiff, the savings is as much as $150, but for a current comparison you should write both companies for their latest prices.

Hardener

Both epoxy systems offer the choice of faster or slower hardeners. Unless you are going to build your skiff in a place where the temperature is 80 degrees or above, get the fastest one. The disadvantage is that you must spread the mixed epoxy quickly so that it won't harden in your roller pan, but fast cure is what you want to enable you to roll on a second coat wet-on-wet and complete your epoxy saturation in one session. And even the fastest hardener is likely to frustrate you when you try to sand your epoxy the day after you spread it, only to have your sandpaper clog. This can be turned into an advantage because such epoxy is still soft enough to cut really well with your carbide scraper. I think more scraping and less sanding is the key to working efficiently with epoxy, especially when using it with fiberglass. Defer your sanding as long as possible. Scrape early, sand late; you'll hear me say it again and again.

Fiberglass

Although you can cover plywood boats with other fabrics, such as Dynel (polyester) or Vectra (polypropylene), none reinforces the wood so well as fiberglass. Most are more abrasion-resistant but this makes them hard to use because they sand poorly; even a sharp scraper has difficulty with some of them. None comes in more than one weight, a disadvantage because different areas of the skiff require different amounts of protection. And all are more expensive. Fiberglasss is much the best combination of structural strength, ease of use, and price. You can make up for its relative lack of abrasion-resistance by adding more of it to high wear areas or by installing wearing strakes.

Fiberglass comes in three common forms: *mat*, *woven roving*, and *cloth*. The first two are designed primarily for fiberglass

Figure 5-5. Cutting a panel to size from a roll of fiberglass cloth.

Figure 5-6. Cutting cloth into strips to make fiberglass tape.

Epoxy and Fiberglass

boats and shouldn't be used on plywood skiffs. Fiberglass cloth comes in several weights, measured in ounces per square yard, and in several widths. The Tolman Skiff requires both 6- and 10-ounce cloth, both in 38-inch widths. You may recall an earlier reference to fiberglass tape. This is simply narrow strips of fiberglass cloth, and although you can buy it already cut, it is much cheaper to cut your own.

To build the 20-foot skiff, you need the following:

- 40 yards of 6-ounce cloth (38-inch width)

- 28 yards of 10-ounce cloth (38-inch width)

In addition to providing structural strength and abrasion resistance, fiberglass cloth prevents plywood from developing fine surface cracks, called checks. Checks develop mostly where plywood is exposed to direct sunlight, mainly the inside of the side panels of the skiff. Unlike the bottom panels, these panels wouldn't normally be fiberglassed. Although checking doesn't seem to cause rot where there is no standing water, such as on the side panels, it looks bad and eventually causes the paint to peel. More and more skiff owners are choosing to have the side panels of their skiffs glassed inside and out. The extra glass adds more weight (about 35 pounds), expense (about $150 in materials), and a small amount more labor, but I think it's worth it. The materials list above includes enough cloth to cover the side panels.

I have carefully worked out the rest of the glass schedule for the Tolman Skiff. Over the years it has proved adequate structurally, and I discourage you from putting on heavier glass or adding more layers. However, feel free to add light (6-ounce) cloth to any unglassed, high-wear areas like the tops of the stringers or the interior of the splash box.

To increase the abrasion resistance of the bottoms of skiffs frequently launched and retrieved on sandy beaches, some owners use the very durable two-part epoxy or polyurethane paints. Some add an additional outer layer of a relatively soft epoxy product called Gluvit (available in many boating supply stores), renewing it as it wears. But for rocky beaches and rivers there is nothing, including extra fiberglass, that will prove tough enough. That is aluminum boat country.

6 | Preparing the Plywood

Once you've made your design decisions, assembled your tools, and bought your materials, you can't postpone it any longer—you've got to start cutting some wood. We'll start by ripping the plywood panels for the bottom and side planking. (We'll wait on ripping the transom panel until the shape of the transom has been drawn on it.) I remind you that the bottom will be made from ½- and ¼-inch plywood, the transom from ½-inch, and the sides from ⅜-inch. You'll use the material left over after you've ripped your panels to make other skiff parts later on. Store it flat so it won't warp.

Ripping the Bottom and Side Panels

It's table saw time—yours or some one else's—but if you don't have one, a Skilsaw will be fine. Rip a 30-inch panel from each of your 4 × 12 × ½-inch sheets. If you're using a table saw, chances are the fence won't adjust to 30 inches, so set it to 18 inches, measured to the side of the blade farthest from the fence. Assuming your plywood is exactly 48 inches wide (check it), you'll end up with a 30-inch panel. If you're cutting with a Skilsaw, mark the uncut edge, known as the factory edge, with a heavy, easy-to-see mark. You will want to put these accurate edges together when you make your bottom.

Let me pause here to give you a short lecture on cutting with a Skilsaw. If you have a good saw with a sharp blade, as you should have, you can cut very accurately. Therefore, saw on your marked line; don't leave any wood—intentionally—to be planed off later. If after you've made your cut you can see your line here and there, plane it off. Don't worry about the parts of your cut where your saw took off slightly too much

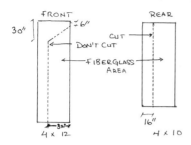

Figure 6-1. Cutting and fiberglassing schedule for
⅜-inch side panels.

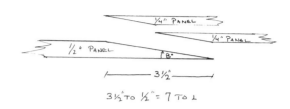

Figure 6-2. Scarf splicing the bottom panels.

wood. These hollows will be filled later with epoxy. There's a Latin phrase for it: epoxii omnia vincit, which translates roughly to "epoxy triumphs over everything."

Next, rip 30-inch panels from the four sheets of ¼-inch plywood, again marking the factory edge. If you are using a Skilsaw, you may want to stack the four sheets, clamp them together, and cut them all at once.

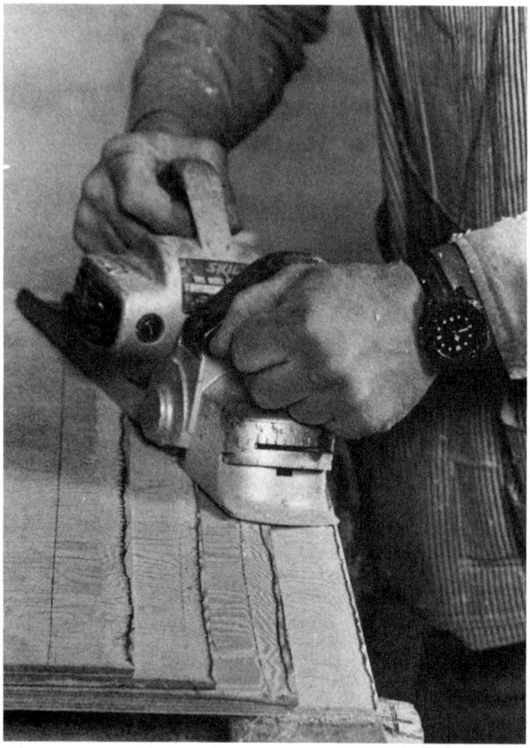

Rip only the 4 × 10 × ⅜-inch side panels, leaving the 4 × 12s whole. Rip a full 16-inch panel from each sheet, leaving a 32-inch panel (minus the width of your saw blade). The 4 × 12 panels will be hung on the boat whole, scribed to fit, and then cut. However, now is a good time to draw lines on them to mark the area you will fiberglass (see Figure 6-1).

![Figure 6-3. Scarfing stair-stepped panels with a power plane.]

Figure 6-3. Scarfing stair-stepped panels
with a power plane.

Scarfing the Bottom Panels

As I've already pointed out, the sharply curved front sections of the skiff's bottom are made by laminating two layers of ¼-inch plywood. But the flatter sections toward the rear of the skiff are made from ½-inch panels, so the first thing we've got to do is to join ¼-inch to ½-inch by means of scarf splices. On the ends where they will be joined, each panel is given a bevel of seven times its thickness, which is a slope of about 8 degrees (see Figure 6-2). I saw these bevels with a fixture made by Gougeon Brothers (the epoxy people) that is screwed to the table of my 10-inch Skilsaw. This fixture makes it easy for me, but it would be less convenient for the one-time, one-Skilsaw builder since it would have to be put on and taken off the saw.

Marking

No matter. It is no great job to remove most of the wood with a power plane and then finish the bevel with a low-angle block plane. (You may prefer to do the rough cutting with a large hand plane, a disc grinder, or even a belt sander.) Arrange your 30-inch panels in three pairs, ½-inch with ½-inch and ¼-inch with ¼-inch, so that the factory edges are side-by-side (to the middle) and the ends are flush. Starting with the ½-inch panels, mark the top faces for beveling by drawing a line across both panels 3½ inches from, and parallel to, one end. Repeat the process with the ¼-inch panels but draw the lines 1¾ inches from the ends. When it comes time to glue the panels, you will leave the ½-inch panels bevel side up and flip the ¼-inch panels upside down as a pair so that the factory edges remain together.

Cutting

To scarf the panels, stack all the panels like stair steps, with the end of each panel on the penciled line on the panel underneath it (Figure 6-3). Clamp the stack and be sure to support the end of the bottom panel so you won't break it when you plane it down to a featheredge. Start removing wood by running whatever tool you're using evenly all the way across the edge of one panel, using the others as a guide. Try to remove about the same amount of wood from each panel in turn. As you cut, the laminations in the plywood will begin to appear as stripes, which you should try to keep straight, even, and parallel.

Do the final planing with your block plane, checking your progress with a straightedge (Figure 6-4). Be sure to remove

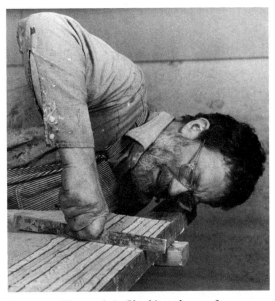

Figure 6-4. Checking the scarfs with a straight edge.

enough wood. Better too much than too little; if there's a slight hollow where the panels join, thickened epoxy will fill it. Remember: *epoxii omnia vincit.*

Preparing the Plywood

Gluing

When you're satisfied with your bevels, arrange the ½-inch panels on the floor so that the factory edges are together and the scarfs, instead of being side-by-side, are staggered about 3 feet apart. This lets the factory edge of the panel opposite align each scarf joint. Try the fit with a ¼-inch panel (make sure the factory edge is toward the center!) by pushing it endways until the faces just make contact but the ¼-inch panel doesn't ride up on the ½-inch panel. If the edge of the ¼-inch panel doesn't cover half—that is, 1¾ inches—of the scarf cut on the ½-inch panel, you need to plane the scarfs a bit more.

Once you're satisfied with the fit, you're almost ready to glue. Put strips of polyethylene sheeting under the scarfs so you won't glue them to the floor and secure the ½-inch panels with a couple of screws or nails so they won't shift. Mark where the featheredge of the ¼-inch panel touches the scarf of the ½-inch panel so you can return it to exactly the same place. Now you're ready to spread the glue and, as always, you'll do it in two steps.

Paint unthickened epoxy onto both surfaces of the joint and brush it until the wood absorbs all it can. Let it soak in a minute or two and apply more if necessary. When there

Figure 6-5. Gluing scarf faces with epoxy.

are no more dry spots, mix up more glue and thicken it with microfibers until it will barely run off your putty knife. Trowel on enough thickened epoxy to hide the stripes on one face of the scarf; if you think the fit is loose, put an equal amount of putty on the mating face.

Clamping

Flip the ¼-inch panel and put it on its mark. Cover the joint with a strip of plastic sheeting and lay a 30- × 4-inch strip of scrap plywood on top so that its edge lines up with the featheredge of the ¼-inch panel. Drive a line of 1⅝-inch sheetrock screws through the strip, through both panels, and into the floor. (As noted in Chapter 3, no pilot holes need be driven for *short* temporary screws, such as those used to clamp layers of plywood until the glue sets.) The screws should be on 6-inch centers and through the middle of the scarf, that is, ⅞ inch from the featheredge of the ¼-inch panel.

Make sure you press down firmly on the plywood strip as you drive the screws. Lots of glue should ooze out of the joint, but you need not waste it. Pick it up and put it on the next scarf after you've wet it out. Similarly, you can find a home for any glue left over from the second scarf; thicken it with microspheres (the white powder), and use it to fill knotholes in your 2 × 8 framing lumber.

You'll have to live in suspense for the next 24 hours while the epoxy cures. Only then can you pick up your panels and find out whether you're a master plywood scarfer. Remove the screws and the clamping strip and turn the panel over. Grind away the excess glue on the flush side of your joined panel and check the joint with a straightedge. If the alignment isn't just right, you may want to sand or plane a little, or perhaps add some putty. Don't be hard on yourself if your scarf isn't perfect. It will be plenty strong, and you're going to cover it with a layer of heavy cloth, then lots of epoxy with sand in it, so no one else will ever know what it looks like.

Cutting Fiberglass Cloth

While your bottom-panel scarfs are curing, you can cut most of the fiberglass cloth to size and make tape out of the remainder. Although you won't need most of the cloth until much later, this is a good time to cut it because you can use your 4 × 12 × 3/8-inch panels for a cutting table by doubling them up on a pair of sawhorses. You should roll up all your cut cloth and tape on square sticks, 20 to 30 linear feet per stick, and your rolls should be tight and even, looking like cylinders, not spirals. Cut 3/4- by 3/4-inch spooling sticks to the following lengths:

- 4 @ 38 inches
- 2 @ 32 inches
- 2 @ 28 inches
- 6 @ 6 inches
- 10 @ 4 inches

Use a felt-tip pen to mark the cloth for cutting. I like a utility knife for cutting along the length of the roll, but I find scissors are handier for cutting across the width. Although you can use a 4-foot straightedge as a guide for your knife, you can save time by buying a 12-foot strip of 1½- × 1/8-inch aluminum at a metal distributor. Whatever the length of your straightedge, the best way I've found to hold it while you cut is to hop up on the table and pin it with your knee as well as your non-cutting hand. Hold your knife at a low angle to the table as you cut. Fiberglass will dull your knife quickly; sharpen it as soon as it fails to cut the glass cleanly.

Some of the cloth will have to be cut into lengths longer than your cutting table. Here's how to do it. Suppose you are cutting the 21-foot by 28-inch strip for the outside of the skiff's sides. Roll out 11 feet of cloth on your 12-foot table, being careful to align the edge of the cloth with the edge of the table. Put marks at 28 and 34 inches across the width of the cloth at each end. (This divides the remainder into 4- and 6-inch tape.) Make your two lengthwise cuts but don't cut the strips off. Roll the cloth strips on sticks of the appropriate lengths, then spin the uncut roll plus the three small rolls as a unit 180 degrees. You can now roll out the remaining 10 feet of cloth, repeat the marking process, and cut it.

Here are the lengths of cloth you'll need. Be careful to match the right weight cloth with the right length, and mark with your felt-tip pen where each roll will go on the boat as you cut it.

For the inner surface of the skiff's sides you will need the following sizes of 6-ounce cloth:

> 2 pieces 12 feet × 32 inches
>
> 2 pieces 10 feet × 32 inches

The remainders will be 6-inch tape.

For the outer surfaces of the sides you'll need the following sizes of 6-ounce cloth:

> 2 pieces 21 feet × 28 inches
>
> 1 piece 7½ feet × 28 inches

The remainders (as described above) will provide 4-inch and 6-inch tape.

For the inner surface of the bottom you'll need to cut the following 10-ounce cloth:

> 6 pieces 5 feet × 38 inches

For the outer surface of the bottom you'll need to cut the following 10-ounce cloth:

> 2 pieces 20 feet by 38 inches

Although you'll need more 6-ounce tape, you should postpone cutting it until you have cut whatever large pieces of cloth you'll need later on. But since you have no 10-ounce tape, cut two 10-foot lengths of 10-ounce cloth. Cut one into:

> 5 strips 6 inches wide
>
> 2 strips 4 inches wide

Cut the second 10-foot piece of 10-ounce cloth into:

3 strips 6 inches wide

5 strips 4 inches wide

Fiberglassing the Side Panels

It is much easier to fiberglass the inner surface of your skiff before you put it together. Lay out the ⅜-inch side panels on sawhorses so you can do all four at once. The 12-foot panels should be turned so that the side you marked for fiberglass is up. This will be your first big epoxy job and you should have your epoxy mixing containers (if you don't have a pump), mixing stick, rags, 7-inch roller, roller pan, and whatever else you can think of close to your panels and set out where you can work efficiently. Be sure you have on gloves and a long-sleeved shirt for protection. Allow two hours of uninterrupted time for this job.

Figure 6-6. Neatly rolling the cut cloth makes later application easier.

Covering the Plywood

Mix epoxy in batches no larger than 16 ounces of resin and 8 of hardener (or the equivalent amount if you are using West System). If you are using a pump, this is about 24 squirts. Mix well; it's impossible to mix too long—unless it goes off in the pan! Wet out all four panels with a heavy coat of epoxy. You will, of course, spread epoxy only on the area inside the lines you have drawn on your 12-foot panels. Return to where you started and look at each panel from an angle at which the light reflects from it so that any dry spots show up as dull areas. Recoat if necessary to make the panels all completely shiny with epoxy. You can now roll on your glass and smooth it out with your gloved hands.

Here's a tip. You'll wipe your hands off on a rag, but they will still be sticky. Dip

Figure 6-7. Using a roller to coat the side panels with epoxy.

them in the container of microspheres. Presto! No more sticky gloves. Sticky gloves are more than an annoyance—they tear easily.

Saturating the Glass

Beginning with panel number one, roll on just enough more epoxy to make the cloth transparent. This takes a nice touch. If you don't have enough resin on your roller, it will pick up the cloth. Too much resin will float the cloth and wrinkles will appear. Take your time.

When you've wet out the cloth on all four panels, stop work for a time and let the epoxy gel a bit. If you've got any resin remaining in your tray, spread it on the first panel you covered. Have a cup of coffee. You don't need to clean your roller, but here's how to preserve it so it won't harden up. With a putty knife and an upward slicing motion, remove as much resin from the roller as possible, then roll it slowly for a few feet on clean plywood using plenty of pressure. You should have an extra roller pan just for cleaning rollers. Put your roller in it and moisten—just moisten—the roller with about a tablespoon of acetone. You can use the resin you got out of your roller by spreading it on your panels with a 1½-inch epoxy brush. Preserve the brush by putting it in acetone in a sealed container.

When you've given your panels a few minutes to gel, drain your roller and pour the acetone into a sealed container—a gallon paint can is perfect—for future use. Wipe the acetone out of your roller with a couple of sheets of newspaper. You can now roll a second coat of epoxy onto the fiberglass, enough to fill the weave of the cloth. The trick is to keep enough epoxy on your roller at all times to prevent it from sticking to the cloth. Before you call the panels finished, look at them again from that light reflecting angle to make sure you have coated them completely and evenly.

Cleaning Up

All that's left is to clean your roller, and this is a good a time to deliver my lecture—or is it a sermon?—on how to do it. I've lost enough roller covers to appreciate that there's a trick to it. The secret is to get absolutely as much epoxy as you can out of the roller before you use any acetone. First, use your putty knife like I described above

Figure 6-8. Rolling the pre-cut fiberglass cloth onto the wet epoxy.

and roll your roller on the plywood. This time pause a minute and then roll it out again. Amazingly, more epoxy will appear. Repeat the process until no more epoxy appears. Then—and only then—pour two tablespoons of acetone over the roller cover and roll it around in your cleaning pan for a minute or so. Wipe the roller completely dry with newspaper. Wet it a second time with acetone and again wipe it dry—absolutely dry. Store rollers by hanging them, so that the bristles won't get crushed. That's all there is to it, but I'll bet it'll take a lumpy roller cover or two before you follow my advice precisely.

As for the panels, set them vertically against a wall after they've cured. You'll sand them just before you hang them on the boat.

7 | Making the Frame Members

As I said in Chapter 1, the Tolman Skiff has a frame, although not a conventional one. There are shelves supporting the gunwales, two stringers running lengthwise to reinforce the bottom, a bowstem, and the two vertical pieces I call rear framing. The transom has a framing member running across it for the motor to hang on. You'll cut all of these framing members from the 20-foot 2 × 8s and, except for the transom member, which you'll set aside for now, you'll putty and epoxy-saturate them before you assemble them on the building jig.

Cutting the Framing Lumber to Length

Put all four 2 × 8s beside each other on a pair of sawhorses. You're looking for one that's straight—that is, doesn't vary to the left or right as you sight along its flat side—for at least 12 feet of its length. Choose the straightest, and if there's more than one, choose the one that is also clearest (most

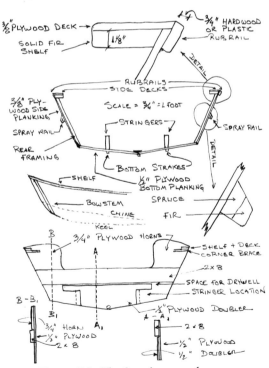

Figure 7-1. The framing members of a Tolman Skiff.

knot-free). Mark the one you select at 12 feet, draw a square line through the mark, and label this piece "rear shelf." Write "transom" on the length beyond the line.

Pick the straightest two of the three remaining boards for the stringers. Square them across at 14 feet 10½ inches and label them. If the last board isn't straight, it doesn't matter—you'll use it for the curved forward half of your shelves. Cut all the lumber on the marks. Stack the stringers and the piece for the transom on the floor of your shop where they will be as cool as possible to minimize warping.

Sawing Out the Shelf and Bowstem Stock

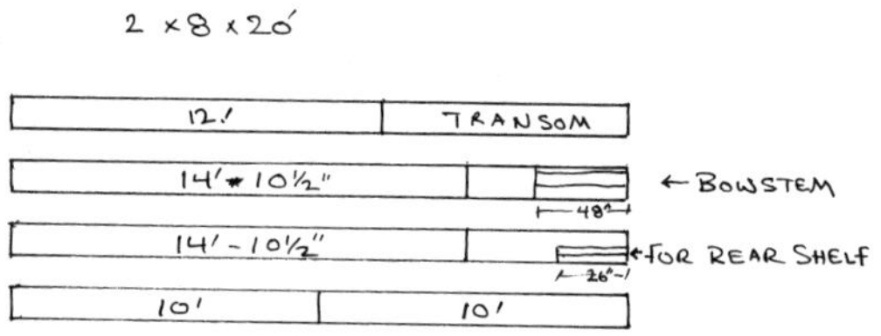

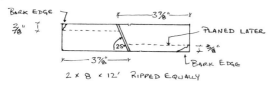

Figure 7-2. The initial cuts to the framing lumber.

Bowstem

Before you can make the shelf or bowstem, you've got to make stock that is wide enough and thick enough by gluing pieces of lumber together. We'll do the bowstem first. Cut two pieces 3½ inches wide and 48 inches long from one of the remainders of the 2 × 8s you cut your stringers out of. Take one of the two pieces and re-rip it so that it is only 1¼ inches thick. Here's a tip: if you are ripping with a Skilsaw, stand both pieces on edge about 2 inches apart on your sawhorses; the piece you aren't cutting will support the table of your saw as you rip.

Put the pieces together, ripped face out, so that you have a piece of stock 2¾ × 3½ inches. Drill two holes in each end for locator screws, which will also hold the pieces together while the glue sets. Turn the pieces so that the faces that were in contact are now up. Mark an x on the face of each and near the same end to show you, when the time comes, which surfaces to glue and how the pieces should be put back together.

Rear Shelf Stock

There are two shelves, left and right, and we'll make up stock for each one in two halves, front and rear. Start making the rear shelf stock by ripping the 12 foot 2 × 8 exactly in half with your saw set at 25 degrees (Figure 7-3). Assuming the 2 × 8 measures

Figure 7-3. The 2 x 8 is ripped exactly in half to make the rear shelf stock.

exactly 7¼ inches, as it should, you can set the fence on your table saw at 3⅞ inches. If you are using a Skilsaw, draw a line at that distance from the edge and run your blade outside of the line so that the 3⅞ face is the wide one. It's best to try your measurement by cutting a piece of scrap before you actually cut your shelves. Note: before you cut, make sure any non-square edges (bark edges) fall on the two smaller faces, which will be planed down later. After you've made the cut, turn one of the pieces end-for-end so that your rear shelf stock becomes a matched pair, a left and a right.

From your remaining scrap rip two pieces 1¾ inches wide and cut them 26 inches long. Turn the pieces of rear shelf stock on edge, beveled edge down, and clamp them together so their ends are flush (Figure 7-5). Mark 24 inches from one end and square across. Your 26-inch pieces will be glued with one end on this line and the other overhanging 2 inches. Drill for two locator screws in each. As you drill, mark the glue faces, the same as you did the bowstem, so that you'll return each piece to its proper place.

Front Shelf Stock

Last, we'll make the front shelf stock by cutting a piece from one edge of a 2 × 8 and gluing it to the other edge. The dimensions of this piece are given in Figure 7-6. Draw these pieces on the 2 × 8s and mark "bow" on the correct end of each. Saw the pieces out, stopping your Skilsaw blade exactly at the end of each line and finishing your cut with a handsaw. Move the cut-out pieces to the opposite edge of the 2 × 8s, locating them exactly the same distance from the ends as they were

Figure 7-4. Rear shelf framing stock detail.

Figure 7-5. Adding the additional piece to one end of the rear shelf stock.

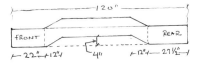

Figure 7-6. Front shelf framing stock detail.

Figure 7-7. Drilling for locator screws for the front shelf add-ons.

originally. Make lines on the 2 × 8s at each end of these add-on pieces so that you'll know where to spread the glue. Drill the ends of the add-ons for locator screws, and, as usual, mark the glue faces so that you can return each piece to its proper place.

Gluing the Stock Together

It's glue time. Turn the shelf and bowstem pieces so that all the surfaces to be glued are facing up. Proceed with the usual two-part gluing process. First, spread a heavy coat of unthickened epoxy with your 2-inch roller, which you can then clean. Add a little more epoxy to what you scrape out of your roller,

Figure 7-8. Clamping the glued front shelves. Not too tight!

A SKIFF FOR ALL SEASONS

thicken it with microfibers, and spread it with your putty knife on one of each pair of mating surfaces. Screw all the pieces together with the locator screws.

Screws alone should clamp the pieces of the rear shelves and the bowstem tight enough, but if the long pieces of the front shelves don't make complete contact, you'll have to use clamps. Too much pressure will squeeze out too much glue; clamp lightly, and if gaps remain, fill them. Maybe you can pick up enough squeezed out glue to do the job. If the two pieces of the front shelf don't lie in the same plane (sighting down them turned on edge), you can force the smaller piece over to match up with the larger one by driving a 6d nail through its face at 45 degrees.

Lofting the Shelves

While your glued-up stock is curing, you can loft your shelves (lofting is a boatbuilder's term for doing a life-size drawing). You've got to draw 'em to saw 'em, they say. Lay down end-to-end two 4 × 8 sheets of clean plywood, or other material you can draw on, and tack them to the floor. If your floor is concrete or you have no floor, your sheets need to be heavy enough material to hold screws (because you'll be screwing your shelves to them) and supported by a simple 2 × 4 frame underneath. There must be at least 4 feet of space beyond one end of the sheets, and make sure the long edges of the sheets make a straight line.

To draw the shelf, you are going to make a line of dots. The position of each dot is determined by one measurement (x) taken from the end of the plywood sheets and a second measurement (y) taken from the long edge of the sheets. These measurements are given in the table in Figure 7-9. Once you've made the dots, you'll connect them with a smoothly curved line drawn with the aid of a long, flexible piece of wood called a batten. There are two sets of y values, called y-1 and y-2. The y-1 values, when put together with the x values, give you the inner shelf line, and the y-2 values give you the outer line. I think you can see already that you'll draw each line connecting only y-1 dots with other y-1 dots or y-2 dots with y-2 dots.

Here's how you actually put these x and y values on your plywood. If you are right-handed, it is easiest to start by hooking the end of your tape on the lower right corner of your plywood. (You then must have 4 feet of space beyond the left end of your sheets.) Mark the x values, starting with the lowest, along the bottom edge of your sheets. Returning to the first x value, square up with your framing square and locate the first y value on this line. This is your first dot. Locate the rest of them the same way. As the y values get bigger, you'll find your framing square isn't long enough. Be very accurate when you extend your square lines. The easiest way is to use a drywall square, which has a 4-foot blade.

The next step is to drive 3d nails squarely through each point. Before you draw your curved lines, use a straightedge or chalk line to connect the last two points in each

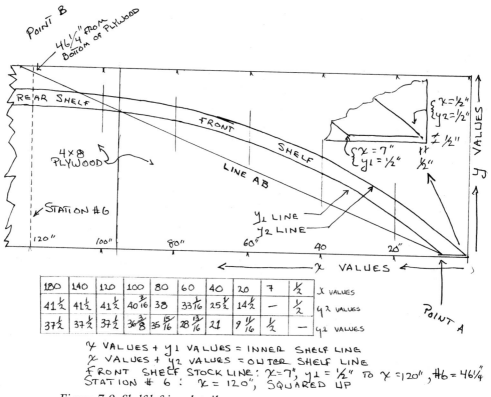

Figure 7-9. Shelf lofting detail.

180	140	120	100	80	60	40	20	7	½	X VALUES
41½	41½	41½	40 3/16	38	33 1/16	25½	14½	—	½	Y1 VALUES
37½	37½	37½	36 3/8	35 15/16	28 13/16	21	9 4/16	½	—	Y2 VALUES

X VALUES + Y1 VALUES = INNER SHELF LINE
X VALUES + Y2 VALUES = OUTER SHELF LINE
FRONT SHELF STOCK LINE: X=7", Y1 = ½" TO X =120", #6 = 46¼"
STATION # 6 : X = 120", SQUARED UP

line (at the left end of your drawing). Bend your batten around the nails, holding it in place with weights or clamps. As you trace along the batten, hold the last foot or so of it on the straight line you've already drawn, to make the transition smooth. (If you don't have a knot-free piece of lumber about 12 feet long on hand to rip a batten out of, you'll have to buy one. I suggest one ¼ × 1 inch instead of one that's square. You'll see why later on in the project.)

You'll need to draw two more lines, both of them straight. The first we'll call AB. Point A is the first value for x and y-1. Point B is 46¼ inches from the bottom of the plywood sheet. Connect them with a straight line. This line represents the joint between the front half of the shelf and the rear half. The second line is called Station 6 and is simply a square line drawn up from the bottom of the sheet 120 inches from the right edge. It is a reference line you'll use later to locate the shelf on the building jig.

Transferring the Lofting to the Shelf Stock

Back out the locator screws from the shelf stock as soon as the glue sets. The longer they stay in, the greater the risk of breaking them as you unscrew them. Don't forget to remove the nails if you used any. You now have two choices: you can transfer the shelf lines directly to your shelf stock, or you can transfer them to ¼-inch plywood patterns, which you can then trace around. You will want to make patterns if you plan on building more than one skiff because it will save you time. For a single skiff, you may still want to make patterns for greater accuracy. Let me explain.

Your lofting represents only the left shelf of your skiff (if you started putting the x and y values on from the right). When you transfer the drawing to the stock, you will get the right shelf (it transfers as a mirror image). To draw the left shelf on your stock, you will turn the right shelf upside down after you've cut it and trace around it, but when you use one shelf as pattern for the other, any inaccuracy in the first shelf will be transferred to the second. The alternative is to make a plywood pattern of the shelf from the lofting that you can use to draw either shelf by flipping it over. A pattern made of ¼-inch plywood is more accurate because you can saw wide of the lines and then plane the wood down to them. Although planing the thin plywood is easy, making a pattern for just one boat does take more time and requires extra material. I'll let you decide which way to go.

Before transferring your lofting to your front shelf stock, put both pieces on your sawhorses so that the ends you've marked "bow" are pointing the same way and the pieces are in the position they will take in the finished skiff. Look at the top and bottom of your stock and mark the best side "top" (⅜ inch will later be planed off the bottoms.)

The first step in transferring your lofting is to lay 3d nails on their sides on your lofting so that their heads are aligned with the x values (Figure 7-10). Tap them into the wood so that about half their heads are imbedded. All set?

Now take your front shelf stock (or your

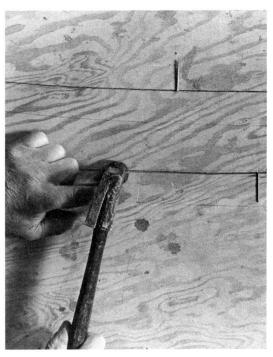

Figure 7-10. Imbedding the heads of 3d nails on the lofted lines to transfer them to the shelf stock.

Figure 7-11. Tapping the front shelf stock to get the nail impressions.

Figure 7-12. Marking the AB line on the rear shelf stock.

pattern plywood, which should be made into a 1- × 10-foot plank), turn it topside down, making sure the end marked bow is forward, and lay it gently on the nail heads so that its lower edge is aligned perfectly with line AB on the lofting. Tap the shelf stock with your hammer (or walk on it) so that the nail heads make impressions on its bottom side. (The person who thought of this should have gotten a Nobel prize.) One more thing: put marks on the bottom edge of the shelf stock along line AB where the lines for the rear half of the shelf meet it.

As you doubtless have already guessed, you now draw your shelf by turning your stock upside down, driving nails into the impressions left by the nail heads, and clamping on your batten. At the rear of your shelf (line AB) you can bring the marks you made on the edge around to the face. These will be the final marks to put your batten on as you draw your lines. Don't worry about drawing the line where the shelf will be cut at the bow, that is, were it meets the other shelf. After you saw out the general shape of your shelf, you can put it back on the lofting and pick up this line by using the edge of the plywood as a reference.

You'll pick up the lines on the rear shelf stock in much the same way, but you only need to imbed the nail heads in the curved part of the lines on the lofting. Place the shelf stock on the lofting so that the larger face is down, the *beveled edge* lines up with the *outer* line (y-2) of the shelf and the *inner front corner* of the shelf stock is just touching line AB. Put a mark on the edge of the shelf stock where line AB appears at its outer edge. Also, put a mark on the edge at the Station 6 line. Press the nail heads into your stock, flip it, and draw the shape of the shelf. Draw line

A SKIFF FOR ALL SEASONS

AB by bringing your mark around and laying your straightedge on it and the inner front corner. Finally, bring around the mark for Station 6 and square it across. Measure back exactly 10 feet along your stock, mark it, and square across; this line marks the rear of the shelf.

Cutting the Shelves

When you make your shelf cuts, follow the same method you used sawing the plywood bottom panels: saw to your lines—but this time don't clean up your cuts with a plane because its easier to do later. Put the front shelf stock on your sawhorses with scrap plywood underneath it (to keep your saw from cutting the horses) and clamp it. I think you can make the outer shelf cuts easiest with a Skilsaw. Saw the outer shelf line at 25 degrees so the saw blade slants under the shelf. This cut strains the best of Skilsaws, so let your saw rest afterwards and go on to the inner cut, which you can make with a band saw or jigsaw (for some reason a Skilsaw doesn't work very well for this cut). When your Skilsaw is cool (I put mine outside) come back to the second outer cut.

You can make all the cuts on the rear shelves with a Skilsaw. When you saw line AB, be very careful to keep your saw table level so the cut is square. The cut on line AB is an exception to what I said above about planing your cuts. Straighten it if necessary with your plane. Cut the shelves off to length at the rear at an angle of 12 degrees, making this cut so that the upper face of the shelf remains the longer one.

Figure 7-13. Cutting the front shelf. Note the angle of the saw blade. Note also the ear protectors.

Figure 7-14. Cutting the rear shelf.

Making the Frame Members

Figure 7-15. Planing the shelves with a thickness planer.

Planing the Shelves

This is the point—and the only point—at which you'll need a thickness planer during the construction of your skiff. Plane the bottom (the smaller face) of your shelf pieces until the stock measures 1⅛ inches in thickness. Two suggestions: before you plane, remove any lumps of glue from the top faces of your shelf pieces, and make several passes through the planer with the lumber (I make four). The planer will thank you for it, especially if your lumber is knotty.

Gluing Up Your Shelves

Your lofting is a guide for gluing the front and rear parts of the shelves together. Turn the right front shelf upside down with its larger face against the lofting. Put a piece of plastic sheeting under the glue joint (line AB) and fasten the front shelf to the lofting with a screw at each end. Your little acid brush is handy for spreading glue on these small areas. Pause a few minutes during the gluing process to give the end grain of the rear shelf time to absorb all the unthickened epoxy it can. Place the rear shelf so that the Station 6 mark lines up with Station 6 on the lofting and don't worry if the front shelf seems misaligned with the rear one along line AB. Drive a screw edgeways into the joint from each side. That's one shelf glued.

Notice I didn't say to fasten the rear shelf to the lofting even though you may have moved it slightly out of position to make the joint tight. The building jig will make the shelf take the right shape later on. Before you glue the second shelf, put more visqueen over the joint. Place the left front shelf right side up on top of the right one and screw it down. It's glue time, and again, before you fasten the two shelf pieces together, position the rear shelf by squaring up from Station 6 on the lofting to the Station 6 mark on the shelf. That's all there is to it.

Fairing the Shelves

After 24 hours or so, pick up your shelves and remove the screws from the joints. Remember, epoxy gains strength gradually, so handle the shelves carefully. Space a pair of sawhorses so that a shelf will sit flat on them (Figure 7-17). At this time you'll work only on the inner and bottom surfaces of the shelves (visualize the shelves in place in the skiff). Fair the inner edges with your block plane. (By the way, is it sharp? It should be like a serpent's tooth for this job.) Begin at the bow, planing with your plane held at about 45 degrees so it will get into the hollow. As the grain changes direction, so will you. Get the curve smooth but don't be concerned if your plane leaves small marks—you can remove them later with your orbital sander. Perhaps you'll want to plane the joint on the underside (the smaller side) of the shelf. When you're happy with your fairing, round over *only* the lower, inside corner of the shelf with your router and sand the two sides you've been working on.

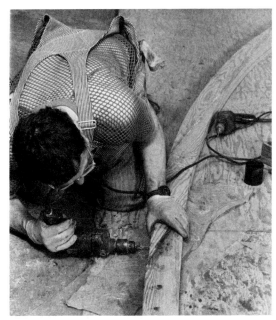

Figure 7-16. Gluing the front and rear shelves together. Note that the shelves are stacked for this step.

Figure 7-17. Fairing the inner edge of the shelf with a block plane.

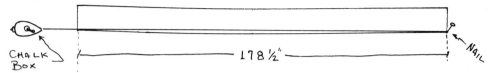

Figure 7-18. Using a chalk line to straighten the top edge of the stringers.

Figure 7-19. Ripping the stringers to width with an 8 degree bevel.

Making the Stringers

Look over the 2 × 8s you chose for stringers and pick the edge of each that is most free of defects. These will be the top edges, and if they show more than about 1/16 inch of curvature, straighten them by snapping a chalk line along the edge and sawing and planing them to the line (Figure 7-18). Then rip them back to 6 inches wide with your saw set at 8 degrees (the wider face will measure 6 inches). Turn one board end-for-end, the same as you did your rear shelf stock, so that they become a matched pair, and place the wider face of each board up. Choose either end of the pair to be the rear end of the stringers and mark them across their wide faces at 78 degrees for cutting. The angle should run in the direction that leaves the

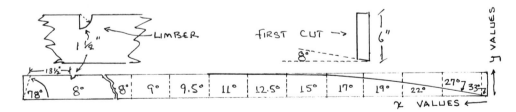

Figure 7-20. Stringer lofting detail.

A SKIFF FOR ALL SEASONS

unbeveled edges of the boards unchanged in length.

You are now ready to lay off the points listed in the table in Figure 7-20 just like you laid off the points for your shelves, except that you'll put them directly onto your stock. Between each pair of points on the stringer, also write the number of degrees that falls between them, as shown on the drawing. This tells you at what angle to saw that section of the stringer. After you've located your points, drive nails in them, bend a batten around the nails, and draw your lines. Don't forget to mark your limbers (water channels).

You will have to stop the cut and adjust your saw table to the correct angle between each pair of points. (Remember that the saw gauge shows the cut angle from vertical while your bevel square shows the angle from horizontal; you've got to subtract every angle marked on the stringer from 90 degrees when you read it on the bevel gauge.) Your saw will probably grunt some trying to make the deep bevels at the tip of the stringers. It helps to back off and start the cut at a new angle. Stop each cut at the end of each section even though there is still some uncut wood on the bottom side of the stringer. When you've finished the curve with your Skilsaw, saw the connecting links of wood with your handsaw.

Use your power plane to smooth out the transitions between the changing bevels, planing one section at a time. Use your bevel square to check the angles, setting it to the next steeper section from the one you're about to plane. By observing the amount of daylight under the blade, you'll know how much wood to plane off. Plane with overlapping strokes that grow longer and longer toward the back of the stringer. Check the

Figure 7-21. Using a batten to draw the curvature of the stringer.

Figure 7-22. Cutting the changing contour of the bottom of the stringer.

Making the Frame Members

Figure 7-23. Using a power plane to smooth the changing stringer bevel.

Figure 7-24. Checking the stringer bevel with a bevel square.

angle often, and when it's right move forward to the next section.

Work on each marked section of the stringer separately, moving toward the tip. As you plane each new section, set your bevel square to the new angle. Don't try to smooth out any hollows you made with your Skilsaw blade; mark them with heavy Xs for later filling. Don't worry, either, about your natural tendency to leave the stringer convex when viewed across the face. In fact, you should make the stringer face increasingly convex as you approach the tip of the stringer, because that's the shape of the hull where the stringer lies against it.

Once you have your stringers faired, round the top edges with your router and cut the limbers. As usual, touch up any rough spots with your orbital sander.

Making the Bowstem and Rear Framing

Bowstem

Rip glued up bowstem stock to $2\frac{3}{4} \times 3\frac{1}{2}$ inches. Use the chart in Figure 7-25 to loft the bowstem directly onto the $2\frac{3}{4}$-inch face of your stock Unlike with the stringers, you'll put the lofting on both sides of the stock, and there are two curves to draw. Saw along the outer line and cut the end at the given angle.

You must now draw a centerline ($1\frac{3}{4}$ inches from the edge) on the curved face you've just sawed. Remove the wood on each side between this centerline and the inner curved line. I do it with a hatchet (Figure 7-

26), but attack it with a saw and finish it with a power plane if you'd rather. Don't be fussy; the stem will be faired later. And as usual, round the square corners and sand it as needed.

Rear Framing

The rear framing members are simply two pieces of 1½-inch stock 2⅝ inches wide and 30 inches long. Round the two corners of the best 2⅝ face on each piece and sand them.

Puttying and Epoxying

Now that you've finished all your frame members, you'll want to fill them all at the same time and, before your putty hardens, to put on two coats of epoxy, wet-on-wet. Mix a loose putty with microspheres and then stiffen it with a little Cabosil. I'll tell you again how important it is to fill everything completely. If there's any dark spot that even faintly resembles a knot, trowel on some putty and strike it off again. You'll be surprised at how often a little dab of putty stays behind in a hole. Look close for hairline cracks, areas the planer missed, edges you've chipped—get 'em all. These are the places that never fill with epoxy alone but show up after you've painted the skiff—telling the world you're a second-rate boatbuilder.

Your 3-inch roller is the tool of choice for putting epoxy on the framing members, but rollers pull wet putty out of the wood. To prevent this, brush some epoxy on each puttied area with your ½-inch brush before you roll. As a fringe benefit, you'll find you can smooth the putty on those devilish places, like holes in corners, that were so hard to do neatly with your putty knife. While you're at it, paint your limbers, thinking as you do it about how much of their life they'll spend underwater. Get my message?

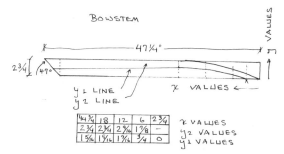

Figure 7-25. Bowstem detail.

44¾	18	12	6	2¾	x VALUES
2¾	2¾	2⁹⁄₁₆	1⅞	—	y2 VALUES
1⁵⁄₈	1⁹⁄₁₆	1⁷⁄₁₆	¾	0	y1 VALUES

Figure 7-26. Shaping the bowstem with a hatchet.

Roll epoxy *only on the smaller face and inner edge of your shelves*, doing the inner edge last to smooth out runs. Spread visqueen on top of your sawhorses when you do your stringers, so you can roll them over and get at all three sides; leave the beveled sides uncoated until it is time to glue them to the bottom. And don't do the end grain of the bowstem, the front faces of the shelves that will go against each other, or the ends of the rear framing because all these areas will be recut. You can use up a little epoxy, however, on the rear ends of the shelves and stringers.

8 | Building the Transom and Center Thwart

The transom is basically a sheet of ½-inch plywood with a 2 × 8 glued across its middle. The plywood above the 2 × 8 and some of it below is reinforced with more layers of plywood. The center thwart is a long, narrow plywood box with sides that extend beyond the ends of the box itself. It has a lid, which you'll make now and install later.

To work efficiently you should build all of these together. While the glue is curing on one, you can work on the others, or you can fill and epoxy them together so you will have to mix glue and clean tools only once. Although you'll actually be working first on one and then another, for clarity I'll describe building the complete transom first, then the center thwart and its lid.

Drawing the Lines for the Transom

Put your remaining full sheet (4 × 8) of ½-inch plywood on a couple of 2 × 4s on top of your sawhorses. You'll be drawing the lines shown in Figure 8-1 on your plywood. You can make most of your measurements by hooking your tape over the edge of the sheet. Where the measurements start inside the edges, I drive a small nail in the starting point and hook my tape over it.

Start by drawing the vertical centerline 42 inches from the left edge of the sheet and a horizontal line 33 inches from the bottom, extending them from one edge of the sheet to the other. Using these lines for reference, you can draw the outside shape of the transom, leaving out the motor cutout for now.

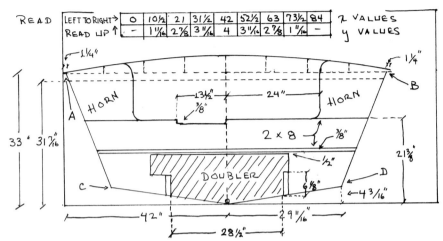

| READ LEFT TO RIGHT → | 0 | 10½ | 21 | 31½ | 42 | 52½ | 63 | 73½ | 84 | z VALUES |
| READ UP ↑ | - | 1¹¹⁄₁₆ | 2⅞ | 3¹¹⁄₁₆ | 4 | 3¹¹⁄₁₆ | 2⅞ | 1¹¹⁄₁₆ | - | y VALUES |

Figure 8-1. Transom dimensions.

The Outline

To draw the arc for the top of the transom, divide the horizontal line into eight equal parts, each 10½ inches long. From these points you can square up and lay off the vertical distances (y values) given in the table in Figure 8-1. This gives you a line of points much the same as the ones you made to draw the shelves. Drive 3d nails into these points, bend a batten around them, and draw the arc.

To draw the bottom of the transom, measure 29¹¹⁄₁₆ inches to the right and left of the centerline and from these points square up and lay off 4³⁄₁₆ inches from the edge. Connect these points, labeled C and D on the drawing, to the bottom of the centerline. You'll find that these lines you have drawn are 30 inches long, the width of your bottom panels.

Locate points A and B on the horizontal line, using the measurements given in the drawing. Draw straight lines from A to C and from B to D. This completes the outline of the transom.

The Cutout

You are now ready to draw the cutout for the motor. You'll remember from Chapter 2, which discussed power options, that the usual motor cutouts are either narrow—28 inches—for one motor, or wide—48 inches—for two motors. Figure 8-2 lists four common outboard power setups. In options 1, 2, and 3 in the table, the cutouts are centered. (Option 3 is also illustrated in Figure 8-1.) In option 4, the cutout is from the centerline 26 inches to the left or right, depending on which side you want your motor.

A SKIFF FOR ALL SEASONS

(Most owners choosing to offset their motors move them to the right. Since the drawing represents the inside of the transom, such a cutout is drawn to the left of center.)

Draw the sides of a wide or narrow cutout (or any special cutout you have in mind) on your plywood. Next, draw the bottom of the cutout using the heights given in the Figure 8-2. If you choose options 1, 2, or 4, you can draw a second horizontal line 7¼ inches below the first to represent the bottom of the 2 × 8 you'll glue to the transom.

Option 3 is a special case—and the one shown in the construction photos in this book. It is a wide cutout, and the upper line for the 2 × 8 is at the height you'd expect for twin motors. However, since the main motor is only slightly off-center, there is a 1-inch-deep notch cut for it, extending from the centerline 13½ inches to the left, as you're looking at the drawing. This lowers the motor so the prop gets enough water, but to tilt an outboard, you need 7¼ inches of clearance between the bottom of the cutout and the horizontal shelf you'll install under the 2 × 8 later on. So you've got to glue a 1-inch strip onto the bottom of the 2 × 8 to make up for the notch. If you are building this transom, draw the second horizontal line 8¼ inches below the first to represent the bottom of the widened 2 × 8.

To make your transom pretty, you'll want to round off the two sets of corners, upper and lower, the motor cutout. If you were good at geometry in school, you can do the upper corners with a compass set to draw a circle with a 12¾-inch radius, and the bottom corners with a compass set with a 6-inch radius. Bisect the angles of the corners and. . . well, if you're smart enough to do it this way, you don't need my help. A faster way for the upper corners is to draw an arc on the tramsom using the circumference of a 5-gallon pail; use a #10 can of beans—or anything else about 6 inches in diameter— for the lowers. Push it into the corner so it touches both lines, and draw your rounded corner.

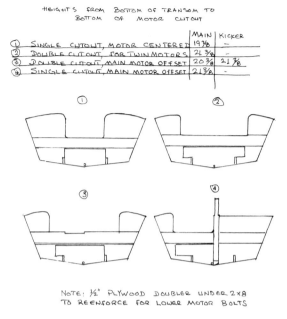

		MAIN	KICKER
①	SINGLE CUTOUT, MOTOR CENTERED	19⅞	-
②	DOUBLE CUTOUT, FOR TWIN MOTORS	21⅜	-
③	DOUBLE CUTOUT, MAIN MOTOR OFFSET	20⅜	21⅜
④	SINGLE CUTOUT, MAIN MOTOR OFFSET	21⅜	-

HEIGHTS FROM BOTTOM OF TRANSOM TO BOTTOM OF MOTOR CUTOUT

NOTE: ½" PLYWOOD DOUBLER UNDER 2×8 TO REENFORCE FOR LOWER MOTOR BOLTS

Figure 8-2. Transom configurations.

The Doubler

Now that you've drawn your motor cutout, you can draw the areas where the stringers meet the transom by taking the measurements off the drawing. The last thing to draw is the outline of the doubler, as I call it. This is a second layer of ½-inch plywood glued to the transom to reinforce it where the lower bolts holding the outboard are placed and to brace the stringers. If you are building a transom for twin main motors, you'll make this doubler wider (Figure 8-2). If you are building a narrow motor cutout, make the doubler only as wide as the inside of the stringers. The top of the doubler will be ½ inch below the line drawn for the bottom of the 2 × 8.

The two areas above the 2 × 8 and at each side of the motor cutout are going to be built up with pieces of ¾-inch plywood, which I call horns, and although there isn't anything to draw, you might make a note to yourself on the transom that this is what's going to happen.

Cutting Out the Transom

First, rip a strip from the top of your sheet of plywood. If you have drawn a wide motor cutout, you will be able to make the strip exactly 12 inches wide for use in your center thwart. If your transom has a narrow cutout, make the cut even with the top of the transom.

Cut the curved top of the transom and the straight part of the three sides of the motor cutout with your Skilsaw and finish the corners with your jigsaw. Make the side cuts on the transom with your Skilsaw set at 6 degrees, cutting the angle so that the upper (inside) face of the transom becomes the larger face. Make the bottom cuts with the Skilsaw set at 12 degrees, again cutting the angle so that the upper face becomes the larger face.

Making ¾-inch Plywood for the Horns

You can make the ¾-inch plywood for the horns out of scrap ripped from your ¼-inch bottom panels. (Of course, you can also use ¾-inch plywood if you have it on hand. If it's ACX, I won't tell.) Measure the areas north of your 2 × 8 and add 1 inch of length and ½ inch of width for good measure. For example, for the transom in the drawing you'll need two pieces 14½ by 20 inches.

Saw out the plywood you'll need. Screw a 2 × 4 to the floor so that when you glue up the pieces, you can square their bottom edges against it. Lay down a sheet of plastic to glue on and spread glue on your pieces. Here's a situation where unthickened epoxy alone will do the job—just make sure you roll on lots so that there are no dry spots. Stack your pieces and screw them to the floor. To make as small holes as possible in the plywood, drive the screws through pads, which I call buttons, made of scrap ⅜-inch plywood cut about 1¼-inches square. The screws should be no farther apart than 6 inches in any direction for sufficient clamping. Once more I'll remind you: press down on the plywood; don't rely on the screws to suck it together.

Widening the 2 x 8

If you are building a transom like the one in this book (option 3), you'll need to make the 2 × 8 you set aside for the transom 1 inch wider. If you want to shorten it a little first, you can, but leave it 2 inches longer than the line you drew for it on the transom. Don't use the stock you ripped from the stringers unless it has knots in it that make it useless to use full length as spray rails. You can rip a 1-inch wide strip from any 2 × stock you have on hand. Glue up the strip and clamp it or screw it to the 2 × 8. If you screw it, remove the screws later. I'll tell you now and remind you later to leave no metal fastenings in your transom.

Cutting the 2 x 8 to Length

Screw the 2 × 8 to the transom with two 2-inch locator screws driven through the 2 × 8 into the plywood. Mark the 2 × 8 for length by scribing along the edges of the plywood. When you cut it, set your saw at 6 degrees and cut the angle so that the side you're cut-

Figure 8-3. Scribing the transom 2 x 8 for length.

Figure 8-4. Routing the top edge of the 2 x 8. Note horns and doubler lying on the transom.

ting from (the scribed side) becomes the smaller face. Round the top outer edge—and only the top one—with your router.

Cutting the Doubler

Cut the second thickness of plywood below the 2 × 8, called the doubler, out of the scrap left over from the motor cutout. (Save those nice pieces from the bottom panels.) You may have to make the doubler from two pieces. I'll leave you on your own, but here's one hint: when you cut the pieces to size, leave stock at the bottom to overhang the transom. Then scribe the extra stock to the bottom of the transom, remove the doubler, turn it over, and cut it from the back side. Set your saw at 12 degrees and cut your angle so that the side you're cutting from becomes the smaller face.

If you're building a skiff that doesn't have a bulkhead under the transom drywell (see Chapter 2), the limbers in your stringers will be at the transom, and the doubler will partly block them. To fix this, chisel a 45-degree bevel on the lower 1½ inches of the sides of the doubler where the stringers come up against it.

Cutting and Mortising the Horns

When you remove the buttons from the ¾-inch plywood you made, you'll notice the screws left little humps around the holes. Sand them off. Now is also the time to smooth and fair the top of transom, from the outer points around the radiused corners and down the sides of the motor cutout. Screw your homemade plywood in place with locator screws and scribe around the transom. Remove the pieces.

Set your saw at 6 degrees to make the outside cuts. By now you know you're going to make the side you're cutting from the smaller face. When you make the cut along the top and inner side, you can go two ways. The best is to cut ⅛ inch wide of the line, put the piece back on the transom, and trim the remaining wood with your router using a flush trimming bit. Your pieces will then match exactly. (If you don't have one of these bits, I strongly recommend buying one, not only for this operation but especially for trimming the plywood side decks to the inside of your shelves later on.) Option two is to make the cuts flush to the line with your Skilsaw and jigsaw, and plane if necessary. After you've cut your horns to shape, round their corners with your router. (You won't, of course, round the edge that will later rest against the hull planking.)

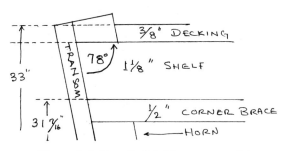

Figure 8-5. Detail of shelf-to-transom joint.

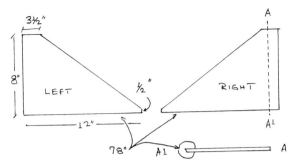

Figure 8-6. Transom corner braces.

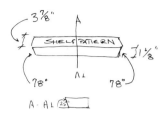

Figure 8-7. Shelf trial piece.

The shelves are joined to the transom by passing through the ¾-inch plywood horns and resting against the ½-inch plywood behind (Figure 8-5). This joint is reinforced by triangular corner braces made of ½-inch plywood that also pass through the horns. Both the shelves and the corner braces meet the transom at an angle of 78 degrees. Visualize this by looking at one of the pictures in this book that shows the skiff side-view. Notice how the transom slants back but the shelf is level; there's your 78 degrees.

Picturing the transom and shelves should help you cut the corner braces (Figure 8-6). Notice that the braces are not identical but are a left and a right. You can make them out of ½-inch plywood scrap from the transom. Then cut a piece of scrap lumber a foot or so long that has the same cross-section as that of your shelves (including the 25-degree bevel). Cut each end of this trial piece square but with your saw set at 12 degrees. (You cut 12 to get 78, right?) Like the shelves themselves, the top, or wider, face should be larger than the bottom face after you've made your cuts. By swapping the trial piece (Figure 8-7) end-for-end, it can represent both your left and your right shelf.

To cut the holes, or mortises, as I call them, through the horns, you've got to draw the edge of the corner brace and the end of the shelf on to the horns. First remove the horns and make marks on the outer edges of your transom where the horizontal 33-inch line meets them. Screw your horns back in place. With your bevel square set at 78 degrees, bring the marks you made for the 33-inch line to the upper edge of the ¾-inch plywood, then around the corner onto the face of the horns (Figure 8-8). Use a long straightedge to draw a line between the two

Figure 8-8. Bringing up the marks for the 33-inch line from the transom to the horns.

Figure 8-9. Using a long straightedge to mark the line across both horns.

Figure 8-10. Marking the outline of the shelf and the corner brace on the horn.

marks all the way across the transom. If you have drawn your 78-degree angle right, the line you just drew should be closer to the bottom of the transom than the 33-inch line.

Draw a second horizontal line all the way across the transom 1⁵⁄₁₆ inches below the line you just drew. Now you're ready to take your trial shelf piece and place it on the horn so that its end lies between the horizontal lines and its outer edge is flush with the outer edge of the horn. Put the corner brace under the shelf and make sure it sticks out beyond the edge of the horn far enough so that you can plane the angle on it later on. Mark the inner edges of the shelf and corner brace and the lower edge of the corner brace (Figure 8-10).

Remove the horns and cut out the outlined area. You may find it awkward to make

Figure 8-11. Cutting the horn on a band saw.

A SKIFF FOR ALL SEASONS

Figure 8-12. Using a rasp to clean out the mortise.

Figure 8-13. Using a bevel gauge to check the angle.

the horizontal cuts with a Skilsaw, yet the table of your jigsaw, like mine, doesn't adjust. I fall back on the band saw, but our famous transom maker, Mary, just lines up the blade of the jigsaw with the line drawn on the edge of the horns and cuts the angle by eyeball. The end cuts to finish the cutout are probably easiest to make with a chisel. When you finish your cuts, check them by reinstalling the horns, inserting the trial shelf piece and corner braces, and checking the angle with your bevel square (Figure 8-13).

Gluing Up the Transom

Assembling the pieces of the transom is straightforward. As I said earlier, all your fastenings should be temporary, driven through buttons. Fasten the 2×8 with locator screws, flip the transom over, and draw two lines that represent the edges of the 2×8. You can now drive screws through buttons on about 8-inch centers. Turn the transom back over to glue the horns and the doubler. Brush out all squeezed out glue, especially any that accumulates in the mortises and in the gap between the doubler and the 2×8. Get a

Figure 8-14. Gluing the transom pieces together. Note buttons underneath for screws holding the 2 x 8 to the plywood.

head start on sealing by spreading this extra epoxy on the end grain of the mortise and the doubler.

Forming Fillets and Coating the Transom

After the glue sets, remove your buttons. Before you coat the transom with epoxy, you'll need to put a fillet of putty above the 2×8. This adds no strength, but it lets you paint and clean easily, and where the fiberglass tape crosses this corner it keeps a bubble from forming under the tape. You can make all non-structural fillets such as this out of microspheres, which are cheap and easy to spread. Mix in as much as the epoxy will hold (you'll be amazed at the volume) up to the point where the putty cracks apart as you spread it. If you have a pump, far less than a squirt of epoxy will make all the putty you need for this fillet—with enough left over to fill all the screw holes and any knotholes in the 2×8.

Forming a fillet is one of those things that's easier to do than to describe, but basically the first step is to get the putty into the corner with your rounded putty knife any way you can. Get a sizable ball of putty on the end of your knife and go for it. When no more putty comes off the knife, reposition the ball onto the end of the knife again by scraping it off on the edge of your putty can and picking it up again.

After you've placed a few feet of putty, step two is to smooth the fillet into final form with your knife held at a constant angle. You'll then have two beads of putty you don't want on either side of your fillet. The fastest way to do step three, picking up these beads, is with the side of your curved knife held at a very flat angle. In tight quarters, where this is hard to do, use your regular putty knife. I keep mine handy between the fingers of my left hand, in which I'm also holding my putty can.

You should leave your fillet in fairly neat form with your knife, but minor imperfections can be smoothed out with your brush as you're putting a heavy coat of resin over it. Although the putty in the screw holes will

Figure 8-15. Forming a fillet.

probably survive rolling, brush over the rest of your putty and roll on the usual two coats of epoxy *on the face of the transom only*. Like the other parts you've already built, you'll sand the transom later.

Building the Center Thwart

Look at the dimensions for the thwart in Figure 8-16. You may already have a 12-inch strip of ½-inch plywood cut from the transom for the bottom and ends. You can get the sides out of the two ½-inch panels left over from the bottom panels. The lid can come out of one ⅜-inch panel remaining from a rear side panel. Did I say ⅜-inch? Sure. I buy my plywood in somewhat different sizes than those in the materials list in this book, and it works out that the only ½-inch plywood in my center thwart is in the bottom and ends.

Therefore, for those of you who will lack some ½-inch plywood because you made the transom with the narrow cutout and didn't end up with a 12-inch remainder, you can make the sides of your thwart out of ⅜-inch plywood. You can get one piece out of your rear side panel remainder, but for the other you'll have to rip a strip from your remaining 4 × 8 sheet of ⅜-inch plywood. Save the second rear side panel remainders for shelf deck-

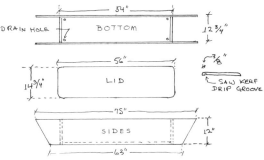

Figure 8-16. Thwart dimensions.

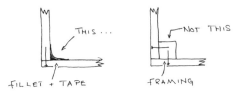

Figure 8-17. Typical plywood joint.

Figure 8-18. Marking joints for nailing.

Figure 8-19. Drilling pilot holes.

ing. You can then use one bottom panel remainder for the bottom and ends of your thwart and make the lid out of the other one.

There's one more thing to add to this complicated materials discussion. The 12-inch side panels of the thwart will be cut off at 75 inches. Rip the 12-inch strip first when you cut one panel. Cut the other off at 75 inches before you rip it. Also cut the top panel (lid) to length before you rip it; do this if the panels are ½- or ⅜-inch.

The joints in the center thwart, like most of the plywood joints in this skiff, are simply plywood glued to plywood without any framing members (Figure 8-17). (Here I'm talking about joints with a constant angle, not the changing-angle, stitch-and-glue keel and chine joints.) Most, including these in the thwart, are also reinforced with fillets and fiberglass, and if you do a conscientious gluing job, these joints are very strong indeed. All of them are held together until the glue sets with 3d nails, usually left in permanently.

Saw out all the pieces of your thwart. Drill the four ½-inch drain holes in the bottom panel (see Figure 8-18) making sure you drill through into a solid wood backup so the panel won't shatter as the bit comes through the bottom. Tack all the panels together, putting two nails in the short joints and at least three in the long ones and leaving your nail heads up so you can pull them. Bottom nails to ends; sides to both bottom and ends.

Unless you have a good eye, I suggest marking the piece you're nailing through with the centerline of the edge you're nailing into (Figure 8-18). For example, when you nail the bottom of the thwart to the ends, which are ½-inch, put a ¼-inch mark across the ends of your bottom to get the nails started right. Drilling pilot holes for your nails

Figure 8-20. Assembling the center thwart after gluing.

is not a cowardly act if you think you can't drive them without splitting the plywood.

When your thwart is assembled, round all the corners with your orbital sander. (It's not necessary to rout them because most are covered by the lid or on the bottom.) Before you disassemble the pieces for gluing, scribe along the edges of all your joints so you'll know where to spread your glue. Last, make a different number of slash marks across each joint so that you can reassemble the pieces correctly.

When you glue, it's the old story: the end grain is your main concern, but don't forget to look for glue starved areas on the other side of the joint as well. I use my acid brush, and after a couple of trips over the

Figure 8-21. Oozing epoxy promises a good joint.

edges, it's more a matter of redistributing the glue than adding more. After you add microfiber putty to the end-grain side, take your time; the longer you leave your joint open, the gummier the glue and the less it runs out. Reassemble your pieces and nail them off on about 6-inch centers. Countersink your nails with a nail set and use the squeezed out glue to fill the depressions. Spread any extra glue on the end grain.

Building the Transom and Center Thwart •97

Making the Lid

After you saw out the lid, round the corners by drawing around a 4 ounce putty can. Round the top edge with your router, but merely soften the corner of the bottom edge with your orbital sander. You'll need a groove on the underside of the lid ⅜ inch from the edge to make the water drip off instead of wicking under the lid and into the thwart. Saw the ⅛-inch-deep cut with your Skilsaw on three sides only—the hinge will be mounted on the fourth.

Taping the Center Thwart

You don't need to wait for the glue to cure before taping the center thwart with 4-inch, 6-ounce fiberglass tape. You will tape the interior joints only, and the first step is to put a fillet in all the joints the same way you did the 2 × 8 on the transom. You'll find bringing three fillets together in the corners is a little tricky, but you can smooth them up when you brush on your epoxy. This time brush on a heavy 2-inch strip of epoxy on each side of your fillet as well.

Figure 8-22. Taping the joints inside the center thwart.

You don't need to pre-cut your tape to length unless you want to. It's faster to roll it out, mark the length by pinching it with your thumb and finger, and cut it off in place (Figure 8-22). Wet out your tape until its transparent. You'll find ordinary brush stroking will pull the tape and wrinkle it. Poke the epoxy into the cloth with an up-and-down motion of your brush.

You can now roll on a heavy coat of epoxy over the entire thwart. Don't forget to do the lid. Unlike the schedule for coating wide panels of fiberglass, you won't be able to put the second coat of epoxy on tape wet-on-wet. But before you walk away from your thwart and let it cure, make sure you cut off all those loose threads of glass and pick them out of the wet resin with the tip of your knife. It sure beats sanding them later on.

After the cure your next job will be to feather the edges of the tape. I can't honestly say that your skiff will be a failure if you can see the fiberglass tape through the paint, yet I feel the standard of good workmanship should be that you make the edges of your tape all but disappear. It's not so hard to do. You can sand them, but I think it's much easier to "carve" the outer inch or so of the tape with your carbide scraper. The trick here is to run the scraper blade on the tape with just a little overhanging the wood, not the other way around, to prevent gouging the wood. Since scraping leaves the glue dull, you can tell when your tape edge is feathered down to the glue beyond, or nearly so. You may also want to lightly scrape the whole surface of the thwart to level the epoxy. You should sand the thwart lightly as well, but how much to sand and how much to scrape I'll leave up to you.

Fill all your tape edges with putty. If your tape is feathered perfectly, you'll lay the putty down and pick all of it back up again. If

Figure 8-23. Coffee break.

there's still an edge, you'll leave a thin band of putty that will fill it. While you're at it, take care of any unfilled nail heads, footballs (plywood patches), and other imperfections. You could even put some putty on the end grain if it looks especially rough. A second coat of resin should finish your thwart (remember: brush over your putty), but in practice there may be little places you'll want to touch up later when you have some epoxy mixed for another job.

9

Stitch-and-Gluing the Bottom

The bottom is the last part of the skiff you have to make before you can begin putting the pieces together. Sawing the two bottom panels to shape and wiring them together will bend them into the shape of the bottom. To make sure this shape is accurate while you "weld" them together permanently with epoxy putty and fiberglass tape, you'll need a pair of cradles set on a level frame. You'll remove the bottom after the glue cures and convert the frame into a building jig on which to assemble the frame of the skiff.

Building the Frame and Bottom Cradles

The frame is 4 × 16 feet and its top should be 16 inches above the floor. Mine is made out of 2 × 12s with casters at the four corners so I can roll it, but a moveable frame isn't necessary. Yours could be made of lumber as small as 2 × 4s if you put two pairs of extra

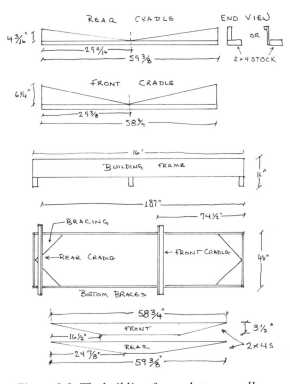

Figure 9-1. The building frame, bottom cradles, and bottom braces for a 20-foot skiff.

•101

Figure 9-2. Squaring the frame.

supports in the middle. If you aren't building on a floor, the supports could be posts made of sharpened 2 × 4s driven into the ground.

The long members of the frame must be straight when viewed along the wide side, the same as the stock for your stringers (Chapter 7). Like the stringers, you can snap a chalk line on them and saw and plane them straight if necessary.

It's very important to make the frame square, which you can do by measuring the two diagonals and making adjustments until they are the same length (Figure 9-2). To keep the frame square, add diagonal braces or plywood gussets at the corners. The bracing should be on the bottom of your frame, out of the way. Put your frame together upside down with the straight side of your lumber on the bottom, square and brace the corners, then flip the frame over.

It's also important to level your frame by putting shims of different thickness under the legs as necessary. Even though your frame lumber is "straight," don't trust it, especially if you only have a short level. Put your level on the edge of a 10-foot plywood ripping and use them together to level your frame, checking the ripping by eye first to make sure it is straight and its edges parallel.

Finally, fasten your frame to the floor so it won't shift during construction. If your floor is concrete, this is hard to do. My suggestion is don't bother; just check your frame occasionally as you build your skiff to see that it is still on its shims. When it comes time too push against the side panels, put a brace from the frame to the far wall.

Cradles

The rear sections of the bottom panels, made of ½-inch plywood, rest on two V-shaped cradles laid across the frame. These can be made of any low-grade scrap lumber—sometimes lumber companies will give you dunnage. You can build them to the dimensions in Figure 9-1 and fasten them to the frame, square with the ends, at the correct spacing. At three or four places between the cradles lay 2-inch lumber loose on the frame to keep the bottom panels from sagging. Beyond the middle cradle lay two or three more pieces of 2-inch lumber, this time thickened with small scraps of ¼-inch plywood, to support the bottom panels where they are made of ¼-inch plywood.

Figure 9-3. Adding bottom cradles to the frame.

Lofting and Cutting the Bottom Panels

To loft the bottom, lay the panels down so that the smooth side of the scarf splice is facing up. Begin measuring the x and y dimensions from the end of the ¼-inch plywood and the uncut or factory edge, using the values given in Figure 9-4. The procedure for drawing the lines is exactly the same as the one you followed when you drew the shelves.

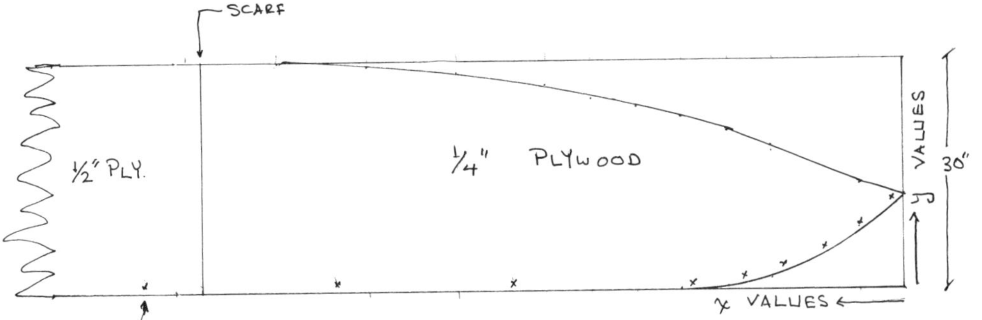

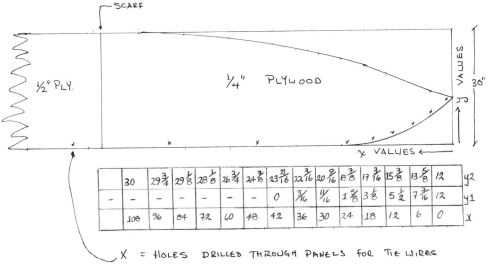

	30	29 3/4	29 1/8	28 1/8	26 3/4	24 7/8	23 11/16	22 3/16	20 9/16	18 7/8	17 3/16	15 3/8	13 5/8	12	y2
-	-	-	-	-	-	-	0	3/16	11/16	1 5/8	3 1/8	5 1/2	7 7/16	12	y1
	108	96	84	72	60	48	42	36	30	24	18	12	6	0	x

X = HOLES DRILLED THROUGH PANELS FOR TIE WIRES

Figure 9-4. Lofting dimensions for the bottom panels.

You'll do your best work sawing the panels to shape if you set the blade depth of your Skilsaw so that it just barely cuts through the ¼-inch plywood. Plane the panel fair in the usual way, knocking off the humps and ignoring the hollows. Flip the cut panel over onto the uncut one and align the factory edges. Match the point of the cut panel to the end of the ¼-inch plywood of the uncut one. Trace around the cut panel on the uncut one.

If you think the chine line—that's the bigger curve you cut—is not perfectly fair, disregard it for the moment. You can correct it with the second lamination of ¼-inch plywood. If, however, the keel line shows hollows, correct them on your second panel by bending a batten to the line and redrawing it. Separate the panels, saw the second, and return it to its face-to-face position against the first.

Stitching the Panels Together

Place one bottom panel exactly on top of the other. Drill a series of holes through both panels with a ⅛-inch drill, ½ inch in from the edge of the keel line. of the panels, starting at the bow, on 6-inch centers. As the keel line becomes straight, you can increase the spacing of the holes to about two feet (see Figure 9-4). Drill a series of ⅛-inch holes through both panels along the keel line on the spacing given in Figure 9-4. For every hole (a hole through both panels counts as one), you'll need a 7-inch piece of soft wire, either

Figure 9-5. Planing the corners off the mating edges.

A SKIFF FOR ALL SEASONS

steel or copper—about 20 feet altogether. I use the steel tie wire used to tie together concrete reinforcing bars. Although it's available in all lumber companies and it's cheap, a roll is much more than you need (unless you drive a very old car). Perhaps you can get a small length from a friendly contractor.

Set the panels on the cradles so that they are resting entirely on the ½-inch plywood. Before getting going with the stitching, there's one more little job. Starting at about the beginning of the curve in the keel line and continuing up to the points, plane the corners off the panels so that they won't slide by each other as you bring them into contact. Just the smallest amount will do. As you plane toward the tips, estimate the changing angle at which the sheets will butt together. When you're finished, place the panels so that their inner edges are touching and the holes in the two panels are exactly opposite each other.

For this next phase of construction you should have a helper. Poke your wires about half way through the holes in one edge of a panel, which I'll call panel one, and bend them so they won't fall through (Figure 9-6). Start at the rear and have your faithful helper raise the edge of panel two. Take the lower end of each wire and feed it back up through the matching hole in panel two. Come back up top each time and twist the ends together with your fingers, leaving the loop loose. When you reach the point where the panels begin to curve away from each other, go back to the rear and work your way forward again. This time, draw the panels together snugly by twisting the wire loops tight with your pliers, pulling as you twist.

Your helper should now move to the bow and take a point of a panel in each hand.

Figure 9-6. Wires inserted in one panel and bent so they don't fall through. You'll need a helper to push bow points together to make stitches tight.

Figure 9-7. Leaving enough wire for the stitch to be secure.

Stitch-and-Gluing the Bottom

As your helper pulls the corners of the panels together, feed the wires one at a time up through the holes in panel two and twist them up fairly snugly with you pliers. For the moment, don't worry if the corners of the panels slip by each other slightly.

After all your wires are in place, the final step is to fine tune your stitching. Gently tap the panel corners into alignment with the heel of your hand as you carefully tighten each wire in turn. You can now cut the twisted wire tails off with your diagonal cutters and flatten them as far down as possible along the joint between the panels. You've got it wired.

Filling and Taping the Inner Keel Joint

Before freezing the shape of the bottom with putty and tape, you must put it in exactly the right position in the cradles. Hook your tape over the bow and run out 101 inches, holding the blade level. Drop a plumb bob (you could also use a level) from 100 3/8 inches to the center of the vee and put a mark (Figure 9-8). Square from this point to the outer edges of both panels. Move the bottom in the cradles until these marks align with the forward edge of the front cradle, making sure the bottom stays aligned in the

Figure 9-8. Locating the correct position for the cradles.

A SKIFF FOR ALL SEASONS

centers of both cradles. Fasten the bottom in place on each side by driving 1¼-inch screws through it into the forward cradle. Cover the screw heads with pieces of masking tape just large enough to keep glue out of the slots.

Before getting going with your fillet, you should snap chalk lines parallel to the centerline of the bottom 2 and 3 inches from it to mark the edges of your tape. You'll only be able to snap these lines from the rear part way forward because the bottom curves upward. Close 'nuf. Now put a mark on the centerline 9 feet to the rear of the 100⅜-inch plumb mark. This is where you will first start your fillet and then your tape. Finally, mark 38 inches forward of the 9-foot mark and square it out to the edges to provide a guide for rolling out your first strip of fiberglass.

Mixing Putty

The fillets you've made so far only added strength to joints where wood was glued to wood, but this fillet, along with fiberglass tape, is all that holds this joint together. I make a special strong putty for this fillet and the similar one at the chine by mixing microballoons and wood flour in even amounts into the epoxy. Wood flour acts like microfibers to make the putty less brittle. I also think putty made with wood flour is strong because it's "resin rich"—a given amount of epoxy will absorb much less wood flour than either balloons or spheres. I don't find much difference between putty made with spheres or balloons; I add balloons in this case to make the putty spread smoothly and because their dark color helps you spot dry areas when you're wetting out the tape.

You will be laying down a 3-inch-wide fillet in the keel joint. To make it stick better, first brush on a light coat of epoxy—don't leave the wood slippery with glue—from your starting mark at the rear to the bow. Use the inner chalk line to estimate the width of the fillet.

This is the time you could use a wheelbarrow to mix your putty in. If you don't have one, mix several ounces of epoxy at a time in your roller pan, then shovel in your wood flour and microballoons with your 3-inch putty knife. Don't mix the putty too dry, which makes it weak, but it should be thick enough not to run off your knife.

Figure 9-9. The right putty consistency for the keel fillet.

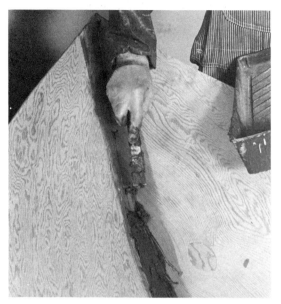

Figure 9-10. Spreading putty into the keel joint, narrowing the fillet toward the bow.

Figure 9-11. Brushing epoxy diagonally to smooth the fillet.

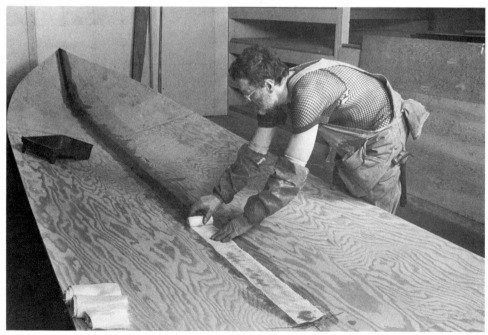

Figure 9-12. Placing fiberglass tape over the fillet. Note the gloves and the protective cuffs to protect hands and arms from the epoxy.

Using your 3-inch knife, start the fillet at the rear mark, leaving the top level for now. Don't work the putty too much with your knife; the more you try to smooth it, the messier it gets. When you get to where the joint starts curving up toward the bow, switch to your 1-inch knife and make the fillet narrower as the vee deepens. At the bow the fillet should have narrowed to about the width of your smaller knife.

Finishing

Mix several more ounces of epoxy and, starting again at the rear, paint your fillet with your 1½-inch brush, angling your stokes at 45 degrees across the fillet, first one way and then the other. You can't use too much epoxy. This should leave your fillet smooth and slightly concave with nice, tapered edges.

You can now roll out 4-inch, *10-ounce* tape over the fillet, overlapping it slightly as you start new pieces. If you've painted the amount of epoxy on your fillet that you should have, your tape should nearly wet itself out, so that you only have to poke in a little more epoxy with your brush to make it transparent. Follow the 4-inch tape with 6-inch, 10-ounce tape and wet it out. Don't forget to cut off and remove the odd strands of glass.

Putting Cloth on the Inner Bottom

If you're a whiz at this business you can follow up the tape right away with your 38-inch, 10 ounce cloth (which should be already cut and rolled). The safe way is to let the

Figure 9-13. Applying the beginning strip of cloth.

Stitch-and-Gluing the Bottom

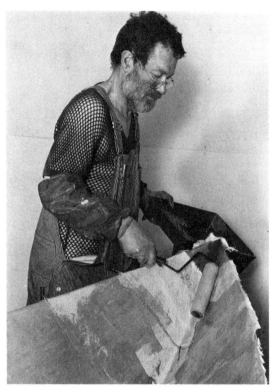

Figure 9-14. Wetting out the cloth at the bow.

tape cure because if you roll out cloth over sticky tape and make wrinkles, you can't smooth them out. If you choose to play it safe, carve the edges and seams of the cured tape with your carbide scraper, not so much to taper them as to smooth them.

There are no special instructions to give you for putting on the cloth except to say start with the rear piece first and overlap the following strips 1 inch. Slash the last strip if you have trouble pushing it down into the curve of the bow. Wet the cloth out thoroughly, putting on enough epoxy to make the surface shiny, but don't put on a second coat.

Trim the cloth on the edges of the bottom with your utility knife as soon as the epoxy cures and smooth the edges of the cloth at the seams with your carbide scraper. The stringers will lie along the bottom at 15 inches each side of center so flatten the seams at each of these areas so the stringers will make good contact.

Taping the Outside of the Keel

At this point the keel seam is very weak, so before you can turn the bottom over to tape the other side, you've got to brace it. Cut the two braces to the dimensions in Figure 9-1 and clamp them very tightly to the bottom as close as you can get them to the two cradles (Figure 9-15). Don't forget to remove the two screws holding the bottom to the forward cradle. You can now flip the bottom in place and set it back down on the cradles.

Snip off all the loops of wire, except the last one at the rear, as close to the plywood as you can. I grind off the wire stubs with a 4-inch grinder, but if you don't have a grinder, you can file them flush. Trim off any putty that oozed through the keel joint. Snap lines from the stern to the scarf splice 2 inches and 3 inches from the joint to roll your tape along. Also, mark the starting point for your outside tape the same distance from the rear as the beginning of the inside tape.

Figure 9-15. Clamping braces to the bottom before turning it over.

As you work on the keel joint, think of the punishment the bottom of your skiff is going to take going through a 3-foot chop at 20 knots. . . . Soak the edges of the plywood in the joint thoroughly using your 1½-inch brush, then fill the gap with microfiber putty mixed very loose so it will run to the bottom of the joint. You'll have to fill the joint more than once, and on the last trip along it leave the putty mounded. Use your brush to put down a band of epoxy and roll out 4-inch, 10-ounce tape, ending it at the scarf splice. After wetting, roll out 6-inch, 10-ounce tape, starting and ending it 2 inches short of the ends of the 4-inch tape. After you have thoroughly saturated the tape and the epoxy has gelled a bit, you can move the bottom off the cradles and stand it against a convenient wall.

Figure 9-16. Rolling tape onto the filled joint.

Stitch-and-Gluing the Bottom

Figure 9-17. Making the building jig.

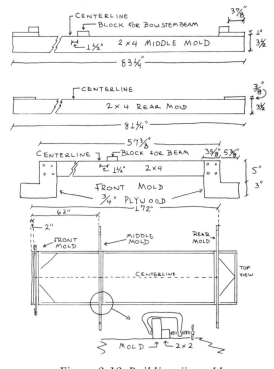

Figure 9-18. Building-jig molds.

Making the Building Jig

Take the cradles and other loose supports off the frame and save the lumber to use again. You'll replace the cradles with molds, as I call them, which are crossbeams that support the skiff's frame (Figure 9-17). Build the three molds, using 2 × 4s that are straight. Make sure you draw centerlines on their upper edges. The molds stand on edge and you'll fasten them to the frame by clamping them to pieces of 2 × 2 (2 × 4s would do as well) screwed to the frame. Screw all three 2 × 2s in their proper places (Figure 9-18). Clamp only the front and rear molds to them, lining up the centerlines of the molds with the centerlines of the 2 × 2s. Before you clamp the middle mold, stretch a string between the centers of the front and rear molds. Line up the middle mold with the other two by aligning its centerline with the string.

You will need a beam to hold the bowstem in position (Figure 9-19). Mine is made out of two 12-foot 2 × 6s nailed together, but any solid or built-up beam will do, providing it is 4 × 4 (two 2 × 4s) or larger. This beam should be as straight as possible in both dimensions and sit squarely on the molds. If your lumber isn't perfect, sometimes you can straighten one piece by clamping and nailing

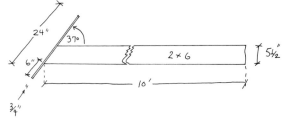

Figure 9-19. Bowstem support beam.

A SKIFF FOR ALL SEASONS

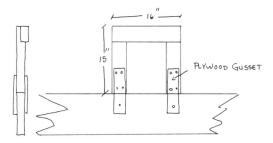

Figure 9-20. Support horses.

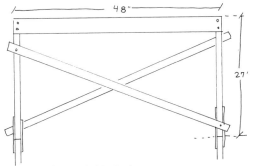

Figure 9-21. Stringer support.

Figure 9-22. Leveling the bowstem against the framing beam.

it to another. Or you can snap a line and straighten an edge in the usual way. Check to make sure that the angled piece on the front end is plumb when you set the beam on the molds (Figure 9-22). Make the beam up and set it aside.

Also make a pair of U-shaped horses to support the center thwart (Figure 9-20). Put the horses on the frame and brace them off so they're solid. Their height is a critical dimension, but you don't need to position them very accurately nor plumb them because you'll line the center thwart up with the mold and the center stringline.

If you have designed your skiff with knees instead of a center thwart, you'll need a single, taller horse to support the stringers. Build it, install it, and brace it off. Again height only is important—you'll set your stringers in place according to the center stringline.

You're ready!

10 | Assembling the Framing and Adding the Bottom

You're going to build the skiff upside down on the jig, starting with the shelf, which rests on the three molds, then adding the bowstem, the center thwart, and the transom. The stringers rest on the center thwart and butt the transom, completing most of the frame and letting you put on the bottom. After the bottom gets its second layer of plywood, you'll finish the framing by putting in the rear framing pieces. That will be a good time to step back and let the glue cure.

Sanding the Parts

I said when you had your jig built you were ready. Well, not quite: everything you put on it will have to be sanded first. I make it seem easier by doing the frame pieces and the transom first and then the skin panels as I need them. There's no need to sand the bottom of the shelves, which I don't bother to paint. Just hit the rounded corner and curved inner face lightly with your orbital sander.

By the way, the best way to clean your orbital paper when it clogs is with a wire brush, and do it before the sanding dust in the paper becomes hard and shiny. You should also change paper frequently; dull paper clogs easily. Save the used paper for hand sanding.

You can sand the large surfaces of the stringers and transom easiest with your disc sander (polisher). As I said earlier, I use only 50-grit sandpaper, but it has to be used very gently at first until it gets a little dull so as not to cut through the epoxy. Move your sander fairly rapidly across the surface, and one time over it is enough. Clean the disc frequently with a gum rubber block.

The disc sands fast but wrecks epoxy even faster. Be especially careful not to damage adjoining surfaces. For example, when you're sanding the transom horns, keep the disc well clear of the edge of the 2 × 8; finish up to the edge with your orbital. Likewise, avoid sanding small surfaces, like the edges of the stringers. Do them and the rounded corners with your orbital. Even with the orbital, corners take a very light touch so as not to cut through the epoxy.

Cleaning

Clean all sanded surfaces thoroughly, first by sweeping, and then with a rag dampened with water mixed with household cleaning ammonia. I keep a 5-gallon pail half full of a solution of ½ cup of ammonia per gallon of water. Rinse and wring out your rag frequently and change the solution two or three times per skiff. To test your cleaning effectiveness, run your palm along several feet of sanded and washed surface—does it come up clean?

Beginning with the Shelves

Lay the shelves on the molds, lining up their Station 6 marks with the *front* edge of the middle mold. Clamp them to the middle and rear molds so their edges are flush with the ends of the molds (Figure 10-1). (For this and the clamping procedures which follow, check the photos to see where to place your clamps.) Pull the shelves together at

Figure 10-1. Clamping the shelves to the jig.

the bow, bring their points together, and clamp a 2 × 4 across to hold them in position. Note that the shelves are not yet pushed down to touch the forward mold. Unless you're luckier than I am, the joint will be open even though the points touch. Run your Skilsaw through the joint—more than once if necessary—taking off wood equally on each side until the joint closes tight (Figure 10-2). Re-adjust the 2 × 4 and clamps to keep it closed.

Drill the edge of the shelves 2 inches or so back from the tips for a 2½-inch screw (Figure 10-3). The hole should be higher or lower in the shelf edge so there will be room for a matching screw coming through from the other side. By the way, these screws and all the ones that follow during the whole construction of the skiff will be sheetrock screws unless I tell you specifically to use stainless.

Let me pause a minute to say that if you haven't already done so, now is the time to set up your five tapered Fuller bits for your different screw sizes and lengths. Match the countersink to the bit diameter and position it on the bit for a given screw length. Remove the countersink and flatten two surfaces on the bit 180 degrees apart to receive the set screws in the countersink. You can grind the flats with a bench grinder or file them. You should set the countersinks for the following screw lengths:

Figure 10-2. Sawing the bow point to achieve a tight joint between the shelves.

Figure 10-3. Drilling the shelf point with a Fuller bit.

- ¼″ (No. 20100125) for 1¼-inch screws
- ⅛″   ″   for 1⅝-inch ″
- ⁵⁄₃₂″ (No. 20100156) for 2-inch   ″
- ⁵⁄₃₂″ (No. 20200156) for 2½-inch   ″
- ⁵⁄₃₂″ (No. 20100187) for 2-inch   ″

Note: bit No. 20200156 is 6 inches long and should be cut off to 3½ inches before you install the countersink.

Assembling the Framing and Adding the Bottom

You *must* drill for all the 2½-inch screws used in the joints in the framing. If you haven't bought Fuller bits, you can pinch the very end of a regular ⁵⁄₃₂-inch bit in your drill chuck and make do. You won't need to countersink for these first two screws in the shelves or the two that follow in the bowstem because they will be removed after 24 hours.

You'll glue your shelves together with the usual two steps: straight epoxy and then epoxy with microfibers, but because you have so many joints to do in a series, mix the glue in two cans, with and without fibers. You can then pick up your squeeze out and carry it forward to the next joint but still have straight epoxy in your other can to spread on first. Use lots of glue because at the end you'll have a home for what's left over.

Here we go. Glue up your shelf joint and clamp it together with your 2 × 4. Drive the first screw and then drill for and drive the second.

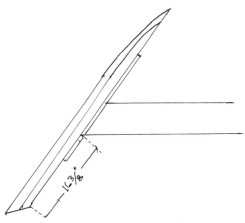

Figure 10-4. Positioning the bowstem on the end of the beam.

Figure 10-5. Lining up the bowstem on the shelf point.

Adding the Bowstem

Screw the bowstem to the bowstem support beam with two screws so that its heel is 16⅜ inches below the bottom of the beam (Figure 10-4). Put the beam and bowstem on the centerlines of the first two molds. You'll find a couple of blocks nailed to the molds half the width of the beam from the centerline will help keep the beam on center (see Figure 10-9). Place the bottom of the stem on the tip of the shelves and gently push down until the shelves touch the first mold and the beam is back down on both molds. Move the tip of the bowstem forward or back until the rear corners of the stem bevel line up with the edges of the shelf (Figure 10-5). Have a look at how the tip of the stem meets the shelves. If there's daylight, scribe a line on the stem parallel to the surface of the shelves showing how much wood to take off. Planing this end grain will test the sharpness of your block plane.

When you're happy with the fit, trace around the stem onto the shelves and then drill a pilot hole for a temporary 2½-inch screw driven nearly vertically through the stem bevel. Remove the stem and rough up the shelves inside the traced outline, then clean away the dust. You should put glue on this surface of the joint as well as on the stem. Don't hurry the gluing process—give that stem time to lap up the epoxy. When you replace your stem, clamp the beam in place on the molds. Drill for and drive a second screw through the stem and clean up your squeeze-out.

Figure 10-6. Making sure the corner brace meets the shelf properly.

Mounting the Transom

Slide the corner braces into the transom mortises and put the transom in place on the shelves. You may have to loosen the clamps and adjust the shelves to get them to fit into the mortises. The outer edges of the shelves won't quite match the transom edges, so pull the shelves out slightly so you can plane them flush later on. Also adjust them, if necessary, so they are centered on the rear mold. Finally, draw lines for gluing on the shelves at the forward ends of the corner braces and on the bottoms of the braces along the edges of the shelves.

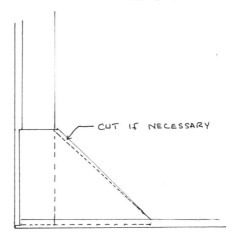

Figure 10-7. Redrawing and recutting the corner brace.

Before taking down the transom for gluing, ask yourself: do the forward inside corners of the corner braces meet exactly at the edge of the shelves (Figure 10-6)? If not, make them meet by redrawing and recutting the 45-degree sides of the braces. While you're at it, round the top and bottom edges of the forward end and the 45-degree side of the braces with your router.

Glue up your pieces and reassemble them. Drive two 2½-inch screws through the transom into each end of the shelves. These will stay in, so countersink them. Now, set the angle of the transom at 78 degrees by cutting a scrap plywood into a 12-degree

Figure 10-8. Plumbing the transom.

wedge and putting it between your level and the transom as you plumb the transom (Figure 10-8). Fix the transom in position with a brace. You can now drive four 1¼-inch screws down through each corner brace into the shelves.

There is one last little job. Pick up your squeeze-out, thicken it with some microspheres, and make fillets between the corner brace and the transom. Also fill over the screw heads. Now put 4-inch, 6-ounce tape over the fillet and epoxy the top (as you are looking at it) of the corner brace.

Placing the Center Thwart on the Horses

Draw a centerline on the bottom and one side of the center thwart by measuring half the length of the box. Set the thwart upside down on the horses with the side with the centerline drawn on it forward. Position the thwart by plumbing from its forward face down to two points on the building jig 2⅜ inches forward of the middle mold. A good way to secure the thwart is by screwing blocks ahead and behind it on the horses. You can now slide the thwart back and forth to plumb the centerline of the thwart to the centerline of the beam.

I hope you've sanded the outside of the center thwart. If not, do so before you mark the bottom of the thwart (which now faces up) for where the stringers will land. Draw two pairs of parallel lines 1½ inches apart on 30-inch centers. To check this, your measurement from the centerline to either inner line should be 14¼ inches.

Mounting the Stringers

If you're building a skiff without a center thwart, draw the same parallel lines on 30-inch centers on top of your single, taller horse after first establishing a centerline on it by

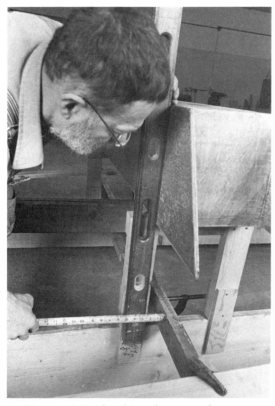

Figure 10-10. Using a wedge between the stringer and the doubler to keep the stringer ¹⁄₃₂ inch high at the transom.

Figure 10-9. Plumbing the center thwart on the jig horses. Note small blocks screwed to the horses to hold the thwart in position and similar cleats positioning the beam.

plumbing up from the centerline on your jig. Put blocks on the horse on either side of the lines to keep the stringers in position.

Put your stringers in position on the thwart (or the tall horse for a thwartless skiff) and butting against the transom. Trace around their transom ends. Remove the stringers and drill two pilot holes per stringer through the transom from the inner face. Return the stringers to the transom, holding them ¹⁄₃₂ inch higher than the top of the transom (Figure 10-10). From the outside of the transom, drill for 2½-inch screws *through the upper pilot hole only* into each stringer.

Before removing the stringers for gluing, mark their bottoms where they rest on the center thwart. Are these areas well sanded? Are they clean? Will you remember to wet them out with glue? You've got to be "meticular," as one of our customers puts it, to build a good skiff.

After you've glued up your stringers and replaced them, drive the screws into the pilot holes. If the stringers suck down flush with the top of the transom, good. If they go down too far, back the screws out part way, lift the stringers up a little, and drill for and drive the lower screws. Then resink the top screws. Pick up the squeeze-out on the transcom and on the center thwart, add some spheres, and make fillets on both sides of the stringers where they cross the center thwart.

Cut the following :

- 4 pieces of 4-inch, 10-ounce tape, 12 inches long

- 6 pieces of 6-inch, 10-ounce tape, 12 inches long

Split two of the lengths of 6-inch tape in half to make four lengths of 3-inch-wide tape. Tape each fillet, starting with the 3-inch tape, then the 4-inch, and last the 6-inch. This is a critical joint; do your best work.

Fairing the Stringers and Transom

If the stringers aren't flush with the transom, plane them flush. Use a straightedge to make sure the top edge of the transom and the stringers are *fair* (Figure 10-11).

A boatbuilder uses the word fair to describe two different circumstances. You say the top edge of the transom is fair with the stringer, for example, when you can lay a straightedge across the transom and the stringer, and it will be fully in contact with both

Figure 10-11. Checking the top edge of the transom.

of them—you can't see daylight between the straightedge and the wood. If it's fair, you can put the bottom panel on and it will fit tightly against both parts. I call this being *fair across*, and it describes the relationship of *two* different parts of the boat.

But what if, after you have faired across, you sighted along the edge of the transom and you found that instead of being straight, as it was supposed to be, you had planed a hollow into it by mistake? Then you would say the edge isn't fair with itself. This second use of the word describes a single part of the boat. To fair the edge, you'd have to plane the hollow out. I would now call the shelf *fair along*. Here's my message: fair along as you fair across.

So if the transom and stringers aren't fair, plane the transom to make them fair across. Check the stringer tops for drips of glue. And now's also the time to sand and clean the inside of the bottom.

Fitting the Bottom

As a final preparation for fitting the bottom, put a piece of 5-inch-wide blocking between the stringers about 30 inches back from their forward tips. You'll have to notch the blocking (Figure 10-13) so that the clamps will be out of the way of the bottom.

Figure 10-12. Frame almost ready for the bottom.

Figure 10-13. Installing blocking between stringers.

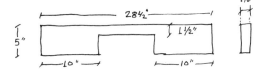

Figure 10-14. Stringer blocking dimensions.

With your helper at the rear end of the bottom, set it on the stringers. Measure from the tip of the shelves 32 inches up the bowstem and put a mark on the front edge. This is roughly where the front tip of the bottom should be after fitting. Slide the bottom to the rear so that it just touches the stem, making sure it doesn't ride up the stem and lose contact with the front of the stringers. Put rough marks on the stem along each edge of the bottom.

Now, stick your head under and have a look. Only the front edge of the stem will be touching the bottom. Push and pull the stem from side to side (as you hold the bottom steady) to help you figure what to plane off to get the parts to mate. Lift the front of the bottom and move it out of the way toward the rear on the stringers, then go after the stem with your power plane.

First, plane an inch-wide flat on the front edge of the bowstem so the bottom won't high-center on the fillet. As you plane, try the

Figure 10-15. Planing the bowstem.

A SKIFF FOR ALL SEASONS

fit, and plane again, keep renewing this flat. Your goal is to make the edges of the bowstem bevel touch the bottom; this should bring two large areas on each side of the stem into contact with the bottom, which is enough of a fit.

Maybe you've been worried by the fact the ¼-inch bottom plywood humps up an inch or so away from the stringers. It'll fit—trust the computer. Prove it by having your helper climb on top and press it down. *Don't* change the profile of the stringers, although you might plane a little on the outsides at the tips.

The final preparation before gluing is to center the bottom on the stringers. With the bottom seated properly against the bowstem and centered on the transom, tack one edge at the transom. Flatter your helper by giving him (or her) a ruler or a tape, whichever you have, so you'll get duplicate measurements, and station him across from you just behind the center thwart. Together, measure along the underside of the bottom from the edge to the stringers. Shift the bottom by moving it at the bow until the distances are equal. When you have it centered, keep it that way with two blocks screwed to the bottom against the insides of the stringers.

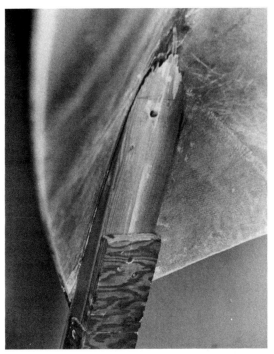

Figure 10-16. The bowstem fit against the bottom.

You can now trace the outlines of the stringers and along the transom for gluing. Before taking the bottom off, mark on each side where the transom meets it so you can return it to position.

Gluing and Screwing the Bottom

Use your 2-inch roller for the first coat of epoxy, beginning and ending with the transom end grain. From here your gluing goes two ways: put lots of putty on the bowstem and transom but recoat the stringers with epoxy thickened with Cabosil. You'll have to experiment with the amount of Cabosil until you thicken the epoxy enough so it won't run but you can still roll it on. When you're finished, clean your roller.

To put the bottom on the stringers without smearing the glue, clamp two plywood scraps to the stringers at the rear (Figure 10-17). Hoist the bottom up, seat it back against the stem, and unclamp the scraps, making sure the centering blocks drop

Figure 10-17. Scraps clamped to the stringers prevent smearing the glue when putting on the bottom.

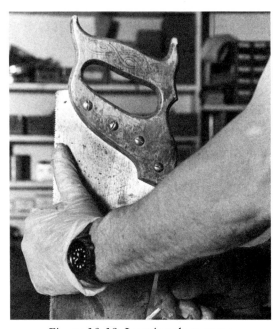

Figure 10-18. Locating the transom at the center of the bottom.

between the stringers. Nail the rear corners of the bottom to the transom, keeping the nail heads well away from what will later become the rear edge of the bottom. Drive four 1¼-inch screws through the bottom into the bowstem.

You can now draw the lines to trim the bottom at the transom. Find the center point by sliding a thin straightedge between the bottom panels (Figure 10-18). Cut the panels off with your saw set at 12 degrees.

Nail the bottom at the transom with 3d nails into the single thickness of ½-inch plywood and 6d nails where it's doubled; the nails should be on 4 inch centers. Snap lines along the centerlines of the stringers from the transom to the scarf splice (locate the centers forward by measuring in from the edges). Screw along the centerlines to the scarf with 1½-inch × #8 stainless screws on 8-inch centers. Drill plumb holes, countersink the heads, and don't screw into the limbers!

Locate the centerlines forward by drilling small holes up through the stringers about two inches to the rear of the tips. You can run a straightedge between the scarf and these pilot holes, but you'll find it can't touch the bottom up front and still let you draw a straight line. Hold the end up, sight straight down, and draw the lines. Fasten the bottom to the stringers forward of the scarf with 1⅝-inch screws.

Important!: stand on the plywood to make it touch the stringer as you drill or screw. Use care; countersink the heads yet don't drive them through the thin plywood.

Take a portable light under the bottom. First, knock out the blocking between the stringers at the bow and unscrew the blocks that kept the bottom centered. Now you can clean up all the squeeze out and fill any gaps there may be between the stringers and the bottom. Don't forget the transom and the stem. Fill any remaining gaps with putty made with half spheres and half fibers.

Laminating the ¼-inch Plywood

Panel One

Begin by checking the scarf splice, centerline, and all over the bottom for glue gobs, raised screw heads, or whatever would keep the layers of plywood apart. It's a good idea to sweep the plywood.

Put the first piece of ¼-inch plywood on the bottom with the factory edge to the center. Align the scarf properly and match the factory edge exactly with the panel underneath. Fasten the panel with locator screws into the stringer at the scarf and along the centerline at the start of the downward curve. Mark the bottom along the featheredge of the panel at the scarf. Note: because this line is hard to see later due to squeeze out, draw

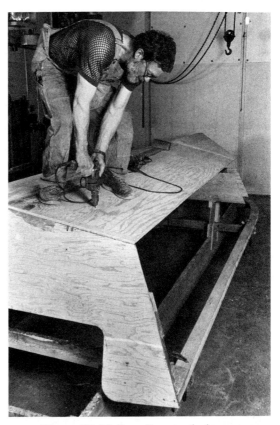

Figure 10-19. Standing on the bottom to screw it to the stringers.

some big arrows with their points on the line. Have your helper bend the panel into full contact while you trace the inner curve of the bottom and the outer curve of the chine.

Remove the panel and cut it—and don't worry that the tip is missing. Roll epoxy (lots!) onto the panel and the bottom with your 7-inch roller. Scrape the roller clean and pickle it in a little used acetone until you need it for the second panel. Coat the scarf with the usual fiber putty and lay down a 2-inch strip of putty along the upper edge of the skiff's bottom near the keel from the scarf to where the curve begins. Also fill the screw heads and putty the forward 8 inches of the tip.

Replace the panel, making sure the locator screws return correctly. Lay sheet plastic and a strip of plywood on the panel at the scarf and screw through it on 6-inch centers, making sure the plywood strip won't interfere with the opposite bottom panel. Bend the panel into place and fasten the tip with two 1⅝-inch screws (Figure 10-20). Again drill a pilot hole up through the tip of the stringer and draw a centerline. This time screw the panel to the stringer with 1½-inch × #8 stainless screws on 8-inch centers.

Assembling the Framing and Adding the Bottom

Figure 10-20. Bending the panel into shape and fastening the tip.

You'll screw the rest of the panel down with 1⅝-inch screws driven through buttons on 7-inch centers. (Hold the buttons back from the keel so as not to obstruct the next panel.) Work from back to front and from keel to chine to force the panel to lie flat against the bottom. As you progress, check your edges to make sure there are no voids between the layers. I'll remind you again: force the panels into contact before you drive the screws.

Panel Two

Before fitting panel two, you've got to fair panel one—from a point just beyond where the centerline of the bottom begins its downward curve to the tip—so that panel two can overlap panel one. To locate this point exactly, put panel two in place against the centerline with the scarf aligned and mark the point on the centerline where the two panels separate. Make a small saw cut into panel one

Figure 10-21. Installing screws through buttons to hold the panel fast for gluing.

Figure 10-22. Making a locator cut for the starting point for fairing.

Figure 10-23. Fairing panel one.

through this point (Figure 10-22) and plane panel one fair from the saw cut to the tip. Replace panel two, drive the locator screws, and bend it down and mark it just the way you did panel one.

If I were you, before I rushed to glue panel two I'd have a dry fit to see if all was well along the centerline. When you're happy with it, glue up the panel and the bottom as before, making sure the centerline where the panels overlap is trowelled solidly full of putty. Then put on panel two and screw it down.

Tips

All that's left are the two little missing tips. I've found that one corner of the smaller

Figure 10-24. Fastening "missing" tips with nails while putty sets.

Assembling the Framing and Adding the Bottom

piece of scrap cut from the ¼-inch bottom panels fits just right. Start with panel one. Hold your scrap in place, mark it by eye along the chine, and cut it. The fit isn't critical; most of it will be planed away later. Glue it up and hold it in place with three 3d nails left with their heads sticking up (Figure 10-24). Lap the second tip over the first, bedding it thoroughly in putty, and nail it the same way.

Installing the Rear Framing

You can locate the two pieces of rear framing by plumbing up to the edge of the bottom from the rear side of the cetner thwart. Measure from there to the inside of the transom and divide that distance in two. That's the center of the flat side of the framing stock, and the edges are, of course, 1⁵⁄₁₆-inches to either side.

To locate the position of the framing on the shelf, plumb down onto the shelf from the center thwart and lay off the same distance. You can now measure the distance between the shelf and the bottom and pick up the two different angles, top and bottom, with your bevel square. I know you're a good woodworker, but still let me caution you: when you lay your straightedge between the shelf and the bottom to pick up your angles, make sure the straightedge runs to the inner corner of the bottom (Figure 10-25). Consider the cuts across the wide face of your framing to be square even though they're not quite. Trust the epoxy to make the fit right.

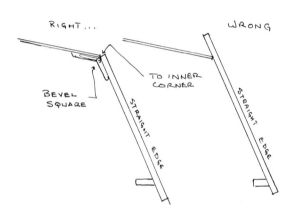

Figure 10-25. Correctly picking up the angles for the ends of the rear framing.

Set your saw to the appropriate angles and cut a trial piece out of plywood, or go cold turkey. When you have your framing cut, put the top end in place against the bottom and drill two pilot holes for 1½-inch stainless screws at 90 degrees through the bottom into the framing. If the framing is wide of the shelf because it's slightly too long, drill for two 2½-inch screws anyway and plane the framing later. If short—but not too—wait till you have no witnesses and raise the shelf. Glue and install.

Making Knees

If your skiff doesn't have a center thwart, it will need two pairs of knees instead, one at Station 6 (move the knee slightly to one side or the other of the mold so you can get the screws through the shelf) and the second where the rear framing is located. Knees are simply rear framing turned on edge with an added piece of ¾-inch plywood that runs across the bottom to the stringer (Figure 10-26).

Make up the solid wood part of the knee and cut the lap for the plywood. The solid wood parts can be fitted just like the rear framing pieces. Cut the plywood part but leave extra stock. Fit the plywood to the bottom and stringer first, then scribe it to fit the vertical solid-wood piece. Glue up the knees and install them. Later, when you turn the skiff over, you can form fillets in the joints and tape the plywood part of the knees to the stringer and bottom.

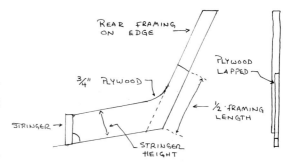

Figure 10-26. Knee detail.

11 | Putting on the Sides

U p till now you've been making pieces of the skiff whose dimensions you knew ahead of time. Unfortunately, you can't tell exactly what shape the bottom will take when you bend it and laminate it, nor the shape of the shelf when it's bent over the molds. That's why you can't cut your particular side panels to one certain shape. Instead, you'll hang the front panel on your frame, mark it, and repeat the process with the rear panel. When you've cut each panel to shape, you'll scarf them together together and hang them on the hull as a single panel. Finally, you'lll fill the chine with the strong red putty you used on the keel and go on and fill every void in the outside of the hull. At that point it'll look like a boat.

Fairing the Transom

Before we get going on the main event, remove all the temporary fastenings: the buttons, the four locator screws, the four screws at the front of the panel, the clamping strips for the scarfs, and six 3d nails at the bow. Cross your fingers and undo the clamps holding the shelves together in the front. Buzz the screw holes with your orbital to make them easier to fill later.

You'll have to fair the sides of the transom and the shelves to get them ready for the side panels. When you fair, make sure you not only fair across, but you fair along also. When your straightedge tells you the shelf, the corner brace, the 2×8, and the transom plywood are all in the same plane, you've faired across. But you also have to sight along the edge of the transom and along the length of the shelf and fair them in those directions, too.

When you're fairing the transom, you'll probably find that the end of the 2×8

Figure 11-1. Marking a straight line on the transom from the shelf to the bottom.

Figure 11-2. Removing the extra length of the thwart sides.

needs planing, which is hard to do without splintering its lower corner. To avoid this, you could plane from bottom to top, but it's hard to plane against the grain. It's better to work against the grain with your Surform or rasp and knock down the high corner as far as you think it has to go. Then use your plane with the grain, whistling while you work.

You can use this idea of knocking down the corner in lots of places. For example, to prevent splintering when you trim the ends of the bottom panels at the back of the transom, sink the nails with your nail set and then round off the corner before you plane the end. If you left much wood when you sawed it off, you may have to round and then plane more than once. When the panels are planed flush, leave this corner rounded for fiberglassing to a radius at least as large as your router would make.

Fairing the Middle

As you work forward with your straightedge (you're putting the upper end against the *inner* corner of the bottom plywood, right?), you'll notice the angle of the shelf soon becomes right—or close enough so the epoxy will take up the slack. Plane the bottoms of the rear framing on the way by if they need it. Draw lines with your straightedge on the four ends of your center thwart side panels and saw them off.

The area around your shelf joint will probably need attention. Plane toward the joint—with the grain—from each direction. Go slow, checking often for fairness across and fairness along, and if you're faced with a choice because you've taken off too much (it's easy to do), always go for a nice, even curve in the shelf even though the angle isn't quite right. If there's a short depression in the curve right at the joint, leave it—the side panel will bridge it.

Fairing the Bow

After you've faired the area around the shelf joint, move up to the bottom and plane the upper lamination even with the lower one. Leave the edge square and the curve fair.

At the bow, your straightedge will tell you lots has to come off both the bowstem and the shelf. I fair all of the transom area with a block plane, but by the middle of the skiff, I am rough cutting with my power plane and finishing with the block plane. Here at the bow, it's power plane country.

Fair one side completely and then the other. Start with the stem, planing toward the tip and working your way higher and higher with longer and longer strokes. At some point your straightedge will lie fair across the stem bevel, but the reading won't be right until you plane the shelf.

Plane the shelf like the stem, with longer and longer overlapping strokes. Notice that (a) your planing angle must decrease as it moves rearward, and (b) as you plane, you've got to maintain the curve of the shelf. Sounds worse than it is.

From here on it's a Catch-22: you can't get the right reading on the stem until the shelf is right, and vice versa. Plane each one alternately until they are both right. As you plane the stem fair, be very careful to take off very little wood—or none at all—along the front edge; sight down it frequently to keep it straight.

On the top half of the stem you can only get a good reading with a piece of ¼-inch plywood, which you can bend slightly to take

Figure 11-3. Checking the bowstem for fairness with a ¼-inch plywood panel.

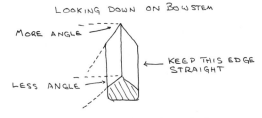

Figure 11-4. The bevel angle on the bowstem changes from bottom to top.

the curve of the side panel (Figure 11-3). Look underneath it and it will give you the fair across and fair along readings at the same time. There's not much I can tell you about fairing the upper stem area except take off less and less wood—to none at all—as you approach the edge of the bottom. You are trying to make the stem bevel twist (change its angle) from bottom to top (Figure 11-4).

Planing the second side of the stem and shelf is exactly like the first except you have to be even more careful not to take too much wood off the front of the bowstem. As you plane close to the front edge, stop and sight along it between every plane stroke.

Marking the Front Side Panel

Sand and wash one 4×12-foot $\times 3/3$-inch side panel. (Do all four panels at once, if you want to.) Before you begin marking the front side panel, you've got to screw what I call a tab to the chine. Tabs take the place of stitches along the front half of the chine and are 2×4-inch blocks cut from 2-inch stock. You'll screw them to the bottom so that 2 inches are sticking out from the chine, and you'll bevel each one to the angle the side panel makes with the bottom panel (Figure 11-6). Although eventually you'll screw seven equally spaced tabs along the front half of the chine, for now cut only the rearmost one and screw it on 12½ inches behind the scarf line on the bottom panel.

Stand the panel on edge even with the bow of the skiff, and drive an 8d nail

*Figure 11-5. Marking the panel
at the bowstem.*

through the unglassed side of the panel 8 inches back and 6 inches up from the lower front corner. Raise the panel and drive the nail into the center of the stem bevel ½ inch above the stem-shelf joint, leaving a third of the nail sticking out. While a helper bends the rear of the panel around the frame, measure the amount of plywood hanging down below the shelf (at about the forward mold). Have your helper raise or lower the panel—he'll have to unbend it—until you measure 1 inch. Screw the rear end of the panel into the tab at the top and put a 6d nail into the shelf.

You can now mark the top of the front panel along the chine. Your helper will have to hold the panel against the bottom at the bow while you are under the bottom scribing the panel. Use the bottom as a guide and hold your pencil (use a carpenter's pencil) perpendicular to the side panel.

Last, mark along the bowstem by sliding your pencil along flat on the opposite bowstem bevel (Figure 11-5), which will give you about ⅛ inch of extra wood. Don't mark the shelf line yet.

Remove the panel and, before you cut it, extend the chine line at the bow by guess. You'll have to extend the bowstem line straight to each panel edge. Make this bowstem cut first and the chine cut second.

Fitting the Chine

Before you can put the front panel on the hull to fit the chine, you've got to put on the remaining six tabs, spaced equally between the first one and the bowstem.

You can now retack the front of your panel to the stem with an 8d nail. Have your helper bend the panel part way around the hull while you press in on the upper front corner. You'll probably have to plane the edge of the panel before you can get it to pop in place below the edge of the bottom and against the tabs. Leaving the 8d nail in place, have your helper unbend the panel and swing it away from the hull so you can plane the edge. When the first three feet or so of the chine fits, tack the top front corner with another 8d nail. You can now fit the rest of the chine the same way. Your helper should use quite a bit of upward force as he bends the panel around each time to try the fit. Putting a light under the hull makes it easier to see what to plane off.

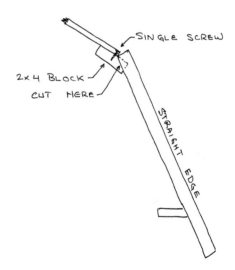

Figure 11-6. Detail of assembly tabs.

I like to get the side panel into contact, or very nearly so, all the way along. There's sometimes a gap for the last foot or so that is hard to close because the bottom has a hard spot at the scarf that leaves it unfair. If your chine comes out this way, you can live with a gap of a strong ⅛ inch as long as the very end closes. (Thank you, epoxy.) When you're happy with the fit, screw the end of the panel to the last tab and tack it to the shelf. The last thing to do is to mark the panel along the bottom of the shelf. Run your pencil on the flat of the shelf, the same as you did at the bowstem, for a little insurance wood. If your pencil runs off the panel in the middle, don't fret—you can fill it easily later on. (Thanks again.)

Marking the Front Panel, continued, and the Rear Panel

You're now going to mark the rear end of the front panel using the rear panel for a square. Align the upper edge of the 10-foot rear panel (fiberglassed surface in) with the long, straight rear edge of the bottom. Push the panel forward until its bottom corner just butts the front panel and its top corner overlaps. Trace along this edge onto the front panel and set the rear panel aside.

Put two marks top and bottom 2⅝ inches forward from the line you just drew on the end of the front panel. These mark the overlap of the scarf joint between the panels. Put the rear panel back on the hull and slide it forward, overlapping the front panel until its forward end rests on these marks. Its top edge must be aligned with the straight run of the chine as before. Tack it front and rear. Note: if the front edge of the rear panel doesn't fall on *both* 2⅝-inch marks, you must correct it until the overlap is even.

You can now mark the rear panel along the bottom of the shelf, transom, and forward part of the chine. Run your pencil on the flat against the transom to add a little extra wood, same as you did on the shelf. Using the rear panel as a straightedge, mark the front panel, connecting the 2⅝-inch marks.

You need one last mark before you take off the panels to cut them. Make a horizontal slash mark across both panels at the joint and midway between the bottom and the shelf (Figure 11-7). This will let you realign the panels after you plane your scarfs.

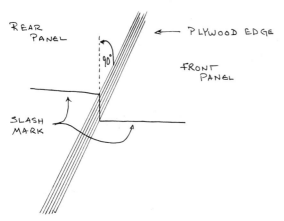

Figure 11-7. A slash mark helps to align the panels after the scarfs are planed.

Remove both panels and cut them. The order of cutting doesn't matter, but—important—make the cuts along the shelf lines with your saw set at 25 degrees, making the inner faces the smaller ones. Before you cut the short section of the chine on the rear panel, extend the line where you couldn't draw it because the panels overlapped. And don't forget that square cut on the rear end of the front panel.

The first side is now ready for scarfing, but you should mark and cut the second pair of panels and scarf both pairs together. The second side is a repeat of the first with one exception. When you mark for the bowstem of the second front panel, put a piece of ⅜-inch plywood under your pencil as you slide it along the stem. This will give you enough extra stock to make the second panel overlap the first when you hang them.

Scarfing the Panels

To plane the scarfs, stack all four panels like stair steps. Before you get after it, there's one tricky point I must make: If you plane away your 2⅝-inch scarf line on your front panel, you'll have no way to line the panels up exactly when you glue the scarf. Therefore, mark a reference line 1 inch beyond the 2⅝-inch line. If the reason for this isn't clear, read on.

Make sure you plane your scarfs with the epoxied side of the rear panel and the non-epoxied side of the front panel facing up. When you glue the panels together, put both epoxied faces down. Dry fit the panels first, aligning the center slash marks on each panel. Also, make sure you have exactly 1 inch—or at least the same distance top and bottom—between your reference marks on the front panel and the featheredge of the rear one. It's a good idea to tack the front panel down and put some reference marks around the rear end of the rear panel so that after you've spread your glue you can return the rear panel to the right position.

Hanging the First Side Panel

When the scarf has cured, flip the panel and clean up the joint. I don't think it's necessary to dry fit the side panel on the hull, but I'll leave that up to you. I'll also leave it up to you whether you hang the first panel or go ahead and make up the second. You make the second panel the same as the first except for one thing: at the bow the second panel laps over the first. Therefore, if you make the second panel before you hang the first, you'll have to mark it at the bow by putting a ⅜-inch spacer under your pencil as you slide it along the bowstem bevel (Figure 11-8).

Before you spread glue I've got to ask it: have you sanded your panels? Make sure you clean the areas of the panel where you'll spread glue. Roll on your epoxy with your 2-inch roller and put Cabosil in the glue the second time 'round on the shelf and bow-stem. Don't forget the ends of the center

Figure 11-8. Using a ⅜-inch spacer to mark the second side panel at the bow so it will properly overlap the first panel.

Figure 11-9. Positioning panel at the bow with a locator nail. Note the tabs along the front top panel.

thwart. Spread putty with fibers on the transom edge, thwart ends, and as much on the bowstem as your fairing job tells you you'll need. Also, wet out the edges of both the bottom and the side panel along the first 2 feet of the chine, starting at the bow, and putty one edge. It will be impossible to get glue into this area after the side panel is hung.

Your job is to put the panel on the hull without leaving "bubbles" where it doesn't touch. I can suggest an order of fastening, but it's up to you to make adjustments to your individual panel. Work from front to back, hanging the panel with the two nails into the bowstem, a screw into the rearmost tab, and a nail into the transom near the top. Then make sure the panel lies against the tabs, putting in a screw or two if you have to. If necessary, push up or down (usually up) on the bottom of the hull between the center thwart and the transom by pushing up on the shelf at the point where the rear framing joins it to align the bottom with the side panel along the chine. Drive a screw into the rear framing to hold it. Return to the bow stem and drive an 8d nail midway between the first two. Then drive two more, equally spaced, on either side of the middle nail.

Next, you can fasten the panel to the shelf with 6d nails, starting with nail one directly below the rearmost tab. Drive nail two halfway to the bow, nail three halfway forward again, and nail four halfway between nail one and nail two. From there on the panel should be lying close enough against the shelf so that you can nail the rest of it from front to back on 8-inch centers.

Nail the transom from top to bottom: 4d nails into the ½-inch plywood, 8d nails into the 2 × 8, and 6d nails into the horns, all on about 4-inch centers. Finally, put two more screws, equally spaced, into the rear framing. Don't forget to crawl under the hull and take care of your squeeze out at the transom, rear framing, center thwart, and bow-stem.

Hanging the Second Side Panel

Before you can hang the second side panel, you've got to plane the first one flush to the bowstem. Here's a good place to knock down the corner before you plane the edge so you won't splinter the plywood. You won't be able to work your plane close to the bottom. I saw this area flush with a handsaw.

From here on you hang panel two just like panel one.

Filling the Chine

Before you fill them, you'll probably have to make the chine joints even by adjusting both the side panels and the bottom. Sometimes the bottom panels will sag in the rear half of the hull. Raise them with props from the floor. Gaps between the bottom and the side panels can be pulled shut with stitches. The problem area just ahead of the bottom scarf splice almost always needs a stitch (Figure 11-10). Maybe you'll want to put more screws into the tabs—or even add extra tabs. Once in a while the side panels are pushed in too far just to the rear of the bow-stem. (Because the sides and bottom are different thicknesses, you can judge this better from inside the hull.) A thin wedge under the tab may do the trick.

Before you fill the chine, paint a light coat of epoxy on the inner edges to help the putty stick. You're now ready for a large batch of microballoon/wood flour putty, making it thick enough so it won't sag out of the chine. Using your 3-inch knife, place the putty in the chine with a squeezing action which leaves it rounded (Figure 11-11). At

Figure 11-10. Tightening the chine with a stitch.

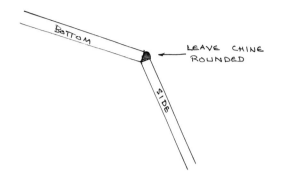

Figure 11-11. Epoxy putty fills the chine.

the bow, fill the chine only level-full; later you'll plane—not fill—the plywood to level it. This will be the only time you'll let putty harden and sand it before you put on tape.

. . . And the Rest of the Hull

Before you fill the rest of the hull, sink all the nails with your nail set. As you sink the ones at the transom, they may raise splinters. Unless you can tap the splinters back flush, break them off and fill the voids later.

From here on you can consider that all filling is cosmetic and use microsphere putty. I don't think I need to detail filling. Just get it all—except, of course, the temporary fastenings into the tabs. Don't let the scarf splices get by you. Check them with a straightedge and if you see daylight underneath, trowel on a wide band of putty with your 3-inch knife.

12 Finishing the Outside of the Hull

Before you start your finish work, remove the stitches (if any) and the temporary fastenings into the tabs. You should also sharpen your block plane, which will be dull from having planed the fiberglass on the side panels.

Fairing the Hull

Although it doesn't matter where you begin fairing, it's best to plane first, disc second, and finish up with your orbital. As usual, I'll talk about each area in turn, but when you do the work, you might want to do all your planing, then all your disc sanding, and so on.

Let's work on the bow first. Start by planing the overlapping side panel flush. You can prevent splintering by rounding the corner before you plane, but leave the bow sharp. Get rid of the hollow bowstem line (Figure 12-1) by thinning out the bottom plywood on each side. Don't worry about this weakening the hull: (a) the stem is under there; (b) there will be four layers of 10-ounce glass over this area; and (c) it's a strong part of the hull, anyway. But I wouldn't use a power plane because it's very important to remove wood carefully, first from one side and then the other, to keep the stem line centered. Eyeball it often! Also, plane the edge of the bottom near the bow to even it up with the side panels.

Once you've corrected the stem profile, you've got to plane a flat surface on it ¾ inch wide for the UHMW bowstrake to rest on. Start the flat about 15 feet from the stern and make a gradual—about 4-inch—transition from vee to flat. It's easy to plane this flat so that it tilts to one side or the other. I straddle the stem and pull my plane to keep it "level" (Figure 12-3). Finally, round the corners of the flat slightly with your

Figure 12-1. The bow before planing.

Figure 12-2. The bow after planing. Note the flat for the bowstrake.

Figure 12-3. Holding the plane level to flatten the vee for the bowstrake.

orbital, which will be enough to let the glass wrap around without bubbling (and leaves the flat slightly less than ¾ inch).

After you plane the side panels back flush with the transom and round the corners, you're ready to shape your chine fillet. Because your disc sander leaves surfaces flat, use it just to grind off the excess; do the actual rounding with your orbital. Wear a dust mask; sanding putty is much dustier than sanding straight epoxy.

Go on and disc the whole hull. If you haven't done so already, feather the edges of the tape on the keel—including the ends, where you'll be adding on more. I finish by fine tuning the hull with my orbital, going over such places as the transom corners and the scarfs. Sweep the hull, or vacuum it, and wipe it down with a damp cloth.

Drawing Lines for the Fiberglass and the Spray Rails

I'm sure you can see additional puttying to do, but restrain yourself so you won't be working in wet glue. Mark all the distances from Figure 12-4 first. Then snap chalk lines along the straight sections toward the rear of the hull and connect the lines for the fiberglass across the transom. You won't have to draw the line for the spray rails on the front half of the hull because the rails will act as their own battens when you put them on.

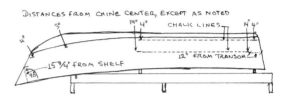

Figure 12-4. The location of the spray rail and the edge of the bottom fiberglass.

To draw the front section of the line for the bottom fiberglass, use a batten at least 12 feet long and more than twice as wide as it is thick. Tack the last 2 or 3 feet of the batten along the chalk line while you use both hands to bend a fair curve through the marks. The wideness of the batten should help you avoid kinks. Have your helper draw a heavy line along the batten with a carpenter's pencil. As you can see, the glass line isn't quite parallel to the chine.

Figure 12-5. Using a batten to draw the fiberglass cloth line on the side panel.

Finishing the Outside of the Hull

Final Puttying of the Hull

If your skiff looks like the ones I build, there will still be a lot of little places that need putty. Here's a little trick: mix your putty about 50-50, microballoons-microspheres, to make the putty pink. Mix it thin and then add quite a bit of Cabosil for smoothness. If you've been using white putty, you can now see what you've done and what you've got left to do. Also, the little places you missed on the chine won't look like air bubbles under the tape, as they would if you used white putty.

I reputty almost everything—certainly all the fastenings—putting it on and striking it off. Leave all your putty smooth so you won't have to sand it.

Fiberglassing the Sides and Transom

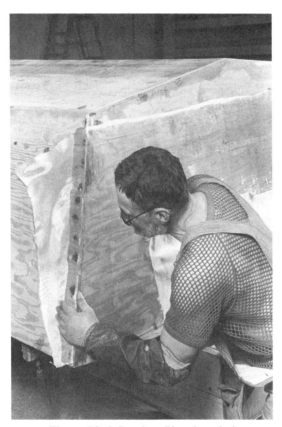

Figure 12-6. Putting fiberglass cloth on the transom.

You should have three pieces of 6-ounce fiberglass, all 28 inches wide, cut for the outside of the hull (see Chapter 6). Put a heavy coat of epoxy on just the area you'll cover with each piece and roll out the cloth. Be careful not to use too much epoxy when you saturate the cloth or it will slide down the hull. Wet the cloth out thoroughly but don't add a second coat of epoxy now.

Start with the transom. You'll roll the upper edge of the cloth 2 inches above the line for the bottom fiberglass (I just guess at it). As you roll the glass onto the angled transom, it will touch at the bottom first, so put a mark on the horn 26 inches below the line to help you get started right. Epoxy the area of the transom you're going to glass and wet out 2 inches around the corners onto each side. Roll on your glass, wrapping both corners, wet it out, and trim it with your knife where the resin ends.

The game plan for both sides is the same. Put a 26-inch starting mark just around the corner from the transom. Roll on your epoxy up to 2 inches above the line. When the line starts to turn down, continue the epoxy line

Figure 12-7. Rolling glass cloth onto the side panel.

level to the chine. Then wet out the whole area, from the chine to the bottom of the plywood, forward to the bow. Wet out the bowstem flat area.

Roll on your cloth, following the epoxy with its upper edge. When the upper edge of your cloth meets the chine, start following the *lower* edge of the plywood with the lower edge of your cloth. Trim your cloth as close to the rear corner as possible, along the chine, and down the bowstem flat. You should turn all usable scraps into 4-inch tape, but here's a warning: don't make tape out of any cloth that has the slightest bit of epoxy on it—it will bubble when you use it.

Taping the Chine and Keel

You don't need to wait for the epoxy to cure on the sides before taping. Continue with 10-ounce tape, first 4-inch and then 6-inch, the same as is already on the keel. Start at the very rear end of the bottom, centering each layer of tape on the chine, but—important—don't let the tape run over the fiberglass line at the bow, roll the edge of the 6-inch tape neatly along the line, even though it may not be quite centered on the chine. Cut the tape off on the center of the bowstem flat. Also, tape the rest of the keel toward the bow, butting it to, not lapping over, the tape on the chines.

Figure 12-8. Rolling epoxy onto the transom tape.

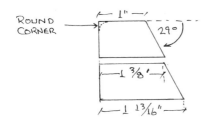

Figure 12-9. Cross section detail of spray rail.

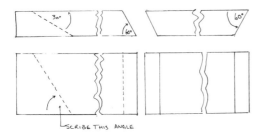

Figure 12-10. Front, rear, and joint detail of spray rail.

You'll tape the joint between the bottom and transom a little differently. Run across with a layer of 4-inch, 10-ounce tape and notch the corners so that the tape butts the chine tape. Follow the 4-inch tape with 6-inch, 6-ounce tape that laps over the chine tape. Last, finish each corner neatly with a 6-inch square of light tape placed so that it is centered on the corner. Don't forget to finish taping the keel at the rear end, butting it to the transom tape.

Putting on the Spray Rails

If you put the spray rails on now (wait till the epoxy cures!), you can epoxy them when you recoat the glass on the sides. Saw out the stock for the rails so that the bottom of the outer layer exactly matches the top of the first layer (Figure 12-9). You should have two pieces (one for each side) for each layer that are at least 12 feet long and knot-free enough to bend around the front of the hull, but you can make the rear part of the rails out of shorter pieces. Use the scrap from the stringers for the outer layer if it is free enough of defects.

You'll need a helper to hold the rail stock in position while you fasten it to the hull. Choose the piece of stock for the front of the first layer of spray rail. Mark the front end and cut the rear end according to Figure 12-10. A power miter box is the tool of choice for all the joining cuts. You'll align the top, or square edge, of the rails with the marks you put on the hull. Put your piece of rail up against the mark at the bow and align the mark you drew on the front of the rail with the bowstem flat. While your helper holds the rear end of the rail, fasten it at the front with a 1⅝-inch locator screw. (Note: Place this screw behind where you will cut the end; you will align this cut with the bowstem flat.)

Have your helper bend the rail around the hull and align the rear end with the chalk line. Sight along the rail and raise or lower it in the middle until it lies straight in line with the chalk line. Mark the front end along the stem for cutting (Figure 12-11) and trace the outline of the rail on the hull. Don't forget to mark the end. Take the piece off the hull and cut it. Drill pilot holes through the outline of the rail on 16-inch centers, also putting a hole at the rear end.

You're ready for glue. Use your 2-inch roller and thicken the second coat of epoxy with Cabosil. While your helper holds the piece in the middle, away from the hull, fas-

Figure 12-11. Marking the spray rail at the bow. Note locator screw positioned not to interfere with the cut.

ten the front end at the bow with the locator screw. Now have your helper raise or lower the rail as necessary to put the top edge on the line. Tell your helper not to move a muscle while you crawl under the hull. Countersink the pilot holes carefully so that the screw heads will lie just beneath the surface. Drive 1¼-inch screws, starting from the bow, as your helper gradually wraps the piece around, pressing it firmly to the hull.

Now that I've got you started, I think you can figure out the rest yourself. Here are some final instructions and tips. Cut the rear end of the first layer (not the first piece) of rail with your saw set at 30 degrees, making the side against the hull the longer side (Figure 12-10). If the points of your screws are sticking through the first layer, grind them flush. Before you put on the outer layer, round the outer square corner (Figure 12-9) with your router. Important!—when you put on the second layer of rail, align the upper (square) edge with the upper edge of the first layer, ignoring the lower, beveled edges.

Fasten the second layer to the first using 1⅝-inch screws, 12 inches on center. Place the locator screw so it won't interfere with your bow cut. Putting screws close by each side of knots will keep the stock from breaking as you bend it. The front piece of rail should be long enough so that its rear end lands where the hull is flat. Joints in one layer should be at least 10 inches from those in the other. Finally, don't cut the front and rear ends of the second layer; run them wild and cut them later when the glue cures.

When you finish putting the rails on, putty the screw heads and fill all knotholes. When the glue cures, trim the ends, round their corners, and sand the upper and outer faces. Reputty if necessary, making sure there are no voids between the rails and the hull, or between the layers. You will finish off the beveled faces when you turn over your skiff over.

Finishing the Outside of the Hull

•149

Putting on the Bottom Cloth

Feather all the edges of your tape and cloth—*except the edges that lie on the glass line*—with your carbide scraper. Fill them with putty if you're fussy. I'll leave the amount of tapering and filling up to you. The least you must do is to scrape, getting rid of the rough edges; the most you could do is to follow scraping with enough filling to make the edges disappear. If you putty, leave it smooth so you can put cloth on immediately without sanding.

Let me say at the start that glassing the bottom is a big job and that you should work fast enough so that your epoxy doesn't become too sticky. Unless you're an old fiberglass hand, I suggest you have a helper. One person can then mix and roll on epoxy while the other rolls out the cloth and cuts it. Have the helper read the following instructions so he knows what's going on.

You should already have your cloth cut and rolled neatly on two sticks (Chapter 6). Wet out one side of the bottom and 2 inches over the keel line onto the other side. Wet out the transom and side panel down to your line. (Go easy on the epoxy—don't let it run.) Finally, wet out the bowstem flat above the line and a pie-shaped piece on the opposite side of the bow.

Starting 2 inches below the transom glass line, roll out your cloth. Follow the 2-inch overlap at the keel until the bottom panel begins to narrow forward of the scarf splice. Then roll out the rest keeping the center of the roll aligned as best you can with the center of the panel. Smooth out any wrinkles with your gloved hands.

Before you wet out the cloth, cut off the extra material at the bow below the line, leaving 2 inches for later trimming. On the opposite side in the pie-shaped area, slash the cloth in two places so that it will lie against the hull. (You actually cut each place twice: the first cut lets you flatten the cloth, and with the second you remove the overlapping piece. This is known as darting.) Dart the cloth also in the upper corner of the transom.

You can now wet out the cloth. The last step before moving to side two is to trim the cloth at the line with a sharp utility knife held at a small angle to the hull. You will have best luck if the epoxy has gelled just a bit, but obviously not so much that you can't pull the cloth away. Trim the pie-shaped area neatly.

The second side is an exact repeat of the first. I should warn you that the new cloth wants to stick to the old near the keel. Lots of epoxy in this area helps, and perhaps you'll want to smooth the wrinkles by moving the slack toward the bottom of the panel.

The final step is to start at the transom on side one and fill the weave of the cloth, recoating the sides while you're at it. To avoid runs on the sides, roll on the epoxy more thinly and go over them twice. Do the spray rails with your brush, hitting them a couple of times as you finish the hull. You'll find the epoxy wicks away from the chine and leaves it resin-starved. Touch up these and other such areas with your brush. A hand-held spotlight will help you spot problem areas.

Making the Bottom Strakes

It's easier to disc sand the bottom *before* the strakes are installed. You'll find the epoxy will cure faster on the bottom than the sides, both because thicker layers will naturally cure faster and because shops are usually cooler near the floor. Therefore, I sand the bottom now and do the sides later. You'll want to feather the edge of the cloth where it overlaps the keel and smooth the seams of the darts with your carbide scraper. Don't feather the glass line along the sides—it makes a border to paint up to.

Rip the strakes to the sizes given in Figure 12-12. You'll make the strake that runs along the keel and up the bowstem from the two vee-bottomed pieces and the ½-inch piece. Rough-cut one vee piece 74 inches and the ½-inch piece 77 inches. Cut a scarf in the end of the 10-foot vee piece (Figure 12-13). A pencil line shows up poorly on UHMW, so scratch the lines with the scribe from your combination square. (Rubbing dust into the scratches will make them show up better.) Cut the other end of the scarfed piece with your saw set at 30 degrees, making the top (unveed) side the longer side. Cut one end of the remaining vee piece with your saw at 30 degrees but with the bevel reversed (Figure 12-13).

The two pieces of stock with beveled bottoms are your side strakes. Cut both ends of these two pieces with your saw set at 30 degrees, making the unbeveled tops the smaller sides. Now round the tops of all the strakes, including those for the keel and stem, with your router. Drill all the strakes with holes 6 inches on center using your $^5/_{32} \times$ 1½-inch drill/countersink. UHMW is tricky to drill, and a drill press makes the job easier. Countersink so that the screw heads go barely beneath the surface.

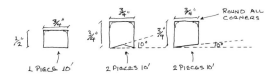

Figure 12-12. Rub strake dimensions.

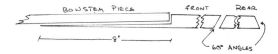

Figure 12-13. Joining three pieces for the keel strake.

Putting on the Bottom Strakes

I use a full-length straightedge when I put on the keel strake, but you can do it with a 10-footer if you use one or—even better—two helpers. Locate the point where the bowstem strake joins the keel strake by measuring forward 180 inches from the rear end of the bottom along the keel. Put the keel strake in place on your mark. Center the strake on the point of the keel by eye: when the top of the strake is level, it is centered.

(You could also center the strake by measuring ⅜-inch from the line between the bottom panels, but the joint line is wide, and what if the panels weren't quite centered?

You're better off doing it by eye. There's an old saying in this line of work: if it looks right, it is right.)

Mark the bottom at the edge of the strake. Drill for a 1¼-inch stainless screw and fasten the strake in place. Note: drill the hole with your ⅟₄₈ × 1¼ bit, going only as deep as the countersunk hole in your strake. Technically the bit is too small for the screw, but it will work.

Go to the rear of the keel, put on the second strake, center it, and mark the edge. Two helpers make the next step easy. Helper one will hold a stringline centered on the screw in the forward strake while helper two holds the other end of the string on the center of the rear strake. Make sure the rear strake is on its mark. You now can center the rear end of the forward strake with the string and mark the edge of the strake on the bottom. Thank your helpers and tell them you'll repay them someday with a ride in your skiff.

Put the rear end of the front strake on its mark, drill the hole, and fasten it. Now you can hold your 10-foot straightedge and the strake tight together and drill all the holes. Put marks along the edge of the strake while you're holding it straight so that you can return it to position. Remove the strake and sweep the hull.

Run a bead of Sikaflex 241 (see Chapter 4) along the center of the vee. (Note: as you build your skiff from here on *all* stainless screws that aren't countersunk and filled should be put in with bedding compound to seal the wood.) You can now screw the strake in place for good. Here's a tip: as you screw the front of the strake, rest the rear on a small strip of wood so as not to smear bedding compound on the hull.

With a few final instructions I think you can take it from here. Cut the rear keel strake at the edge of the rounded bottom corner and bevel the end with your saw set at 30 degrees. Position the bowstem strake by eye and by feel—if you pinch it between your thumb and forefinger, you can actually feel when it's centered. For now, stop the sealant at the second screw hole from the end and don't install the final screw; you'll need to bend the strake out of the way when you plane your side panels at the shelf.

Figure 12-14. Keeping the side strake in line.

Position the side strakes by measuring ⅜ inch from the centers of the screws that fasten the bottom to the stringers. Fasten the ends, pull the strake tight against your straightedge—and so on.

Here's the final step: run a hefty bead of bedding compound along all the strakes—including the ends—and shape it with your index finger. Make sure there are no gaps. You'll need an extra heavy bead to fill the rounded corners under the bowstem strake. Stop the bead for now at the final screw.

Priming and Painting the Bottom

I now prime the hull, leaving 3 inches uncoated below the unfinished spray rails and at the bottom of the side panels. (I use Petit Number 6164 Fiberglass Undercoater.) When the primer dries, you might want to paint the bottom to the fiberglass line, as well. Or you can do all the painting after you roll your skiff over and finish it. More on painting later.

13 | Finishing the Interior

You're ready for another BIG MOMENT: rolling the hull over. (Other big moments will be launching the skiff and selling it.) When it's right side up, you'll tape the inner chines and cap the shelves with plywood, which will complete the basic hull. There are two more things added to every Tolman Skiff no matter what other options the owner wants: a drywell at the transom and a flotation tank/collision bulkhead at the bow.

The skiff we're building in this book will also have a bulkhead under the drywell that makes a second flotation tank with storage, and a storage locker forward that uses the forward flotation tank for its floor. If you want the drywell without the bulkhead and/or the forward flotation tank without the storage locker, you'll find out how to make both in this chapter, but the installation instructions will be found in Chapter 14 with those for the optional bulkhead and locker.

Rolling the Hull

Needed: a helper with a healthy back. I didn't say strong; as you can see in the photos, I can roll the hull with a mere lady, and I'm an old geek. To turn the hull and have it end up where it now is, move the jig 10 feet sideways. (If you're short of space, move it as far as you can, leaving room to stand. You'll have to tip the hull on edge, move it again, and then roll it the rest of the way.) Block the bow up a half inch. This will free the forward and middle molds, which you can remove, along with the horses that held the center thwart and all other supports except the rear mold. Unclamp the rear mold. Put two tires, or other padding, under the shelf on the side you'll tip it toward, one at the transom and the other where the shelf turns toward the bow.

Put the stronger member of your team just forward of the center thwart and the

Figure 13-1. Tipping the hull from the jig.

other near the transom. In one quick lift, raise the shelf to where the hull almost balances. Don't stop lifting when the hull tips off the mold and drops onto the tires. Now one of your team can go around the hull and receive it as the other person pushes it beyond the balance point. Finally, of course, the second person can come around the hull and you can both lower it to the upright position.

Taping the Center Thwart and the Inner Chine

While the hull is still sawdust free, you'll want to do all the filling and taping you can. Scrape away the glass fuzz and fill all the holes through the bottom. Don't forget the ones made by the centering blocks. Fill the screws that go into the spray rails. For the fillets along the chine and the ends of the center thwart where they butt the hull, make your high-strength, red putty.

Make sure you wipe down the hull in the areas you're going to tape. You'll tape the center thwart to the hull with three layers of tape—the same widths and weight of tape you used to tape it to the stringers in Chapter 10. You'll tape the chine with 6-ounce tape, 4 and 6 inches wide.

Beginning at the transom, place a 1-inch fillet in the chine with your 1-inch putty knife. If you're working alone, you better stop at the bow and tape over the fillet before it sets up too firmly. While you're at it, use your rounded knife to run a fillet along the transom from the stringers to the chine and on up the side, stopping 1 inch from the 2 × 8. Now brush your epoxy on the chine, stroking back and forth in two directions at 45 degrees. Roll on your two layers, going light on the epoxy near the bow so the tape won't slide down the hull. The transom-to-bottom joint gets one shot of 4-inch, 6-ounce tape. Finish up that little dab of fillet and tape at the rear end of the keel and glass the unglassed strips at the rear of the bottom.

Figure 13-2. Trimming the side panel at the transom.

Fitting the Plywood to the Side Decks

The Rear Half

Although you'll have to stop work on the hull until the epoxy cures so as not to cover it with shavings, you can rip the plywood for the rear half of the *side decks* from the stock remaining from your rear side panels. (By side deck, I mean the top of the shelf plus the edge of side panel.) Measure the width of your individual side decks in several spots to the rear of Station 6 marks. Take the largest dimension and add ¹⁄₁₆ inch. Rip the plywood

Figure 13-3. Planing the side panel.

Figure 13-4. Notching the plywood decking around the transom.

with your saw set at 25 degrees, making the *smaller* side your deck dimension.

As soon as the epoxy cures, jump onto those tape edges with your carbide scraper. You can now plane your side panels flush with the shelves. Level the shelves in the area of the scarfs if necessary. You'll have to saw the little tits flush that run by the edges of the transom. Fit the plywood decking to the transom by notching it to cover the side panels at the edges of the transom (Figure 13-4). I'd tell you how to do it, but you'll have it done by then. Fasten your decking in place with several 1¼-inch locator screws. Note: your side decks probably aren't perfectly straight. Line up a section of decking *flush with the outside* of the side panels and drive a screw. Bend the decking edgeways to align the next section, drive a screw—and so on. Your flush-trimming router bit will eat the stock hanging over on the inside.

The Front Half

Use one ripping from the front side panels for the next section of deck. Cut it to fit against the end of one rear piece of decking (Figure 13-5) and fasten it in the middle with one screw, forcing it down to the deck. Scribe the underside of the plywood along both sides of the deck with your heavy pencil, which will add a little insurance wood. Remove the ripping and cut it, making sure you set your saw at 25 degrees to make the outer cut. Put the cut decking back on the deck.

Figure 13-5. Fitting the ends of two sections of decking.

You can flop the rest of your ripping over to make the deck for the other side. Fit the rear end first, screw it in place, scribe it—and so on. After you've reinstalled the second piece, fasten the bow ends of both pieces with a screw each. Make sure your stock is flush—or sticks out—everywhere along the outer edge. Now you can lay a straightedge across the bow ends of both pieces and mark them for trimming. Take them off, cut them, and reinstall them.

The Bow

Use the second rear side panel ripping to make the rest of the decking. I know—it isn't wide enough, but read on. Rough cut it to bridge both side decks, flop it across them—against the decking already installed—and scribe the outline, inside and out of both decks (Figure 13-6). Remove it and turn the marked side up.

Figure 13-6. Working toward the bow with the decking.

Now you need a semicircle of cardboard (or whatever) 2 feet in diameter. Place the semicircle so that it touches both of the inner scribe lines and trace around it (Figure 13-7). Saw out the decking, following the semicircle as the inner cut line. This time when you saw your outer lines, set your saw at *30 degrees*. Put your decking in place and use the half-round you sawed out of it to complete the deck (Figure 13-8). Tip: saw the last piece to a point and then rasp it as needed to make the bowstem flat.

Figure 13-7. Marking the bow semicircle with a pattern.

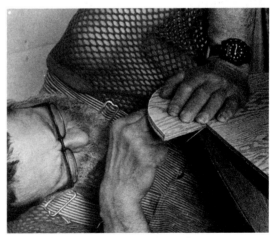

Figure 13-8. Using a semicircular cutout for final piece of decking.

Gluing and Nailing the Side Decks

Before you glue your decking down, there's one more little job to do. You'll notice that the edges of the transom stick up above the deck. Mark the deck line on these transom

Figure 13-9. Marking the deck line on the transom with a chisel.

edges with a chisel (Figure 13-9), then take off the two rear pieces of decking to make room to plane the transom. First, knock the corners off with a rasp and then plane the top edge of the transom so that its angle changes gradually to meet the side decks.

So that your deck joints won't be glue-starved, roll epoxy on the decking first, then on the hull, and again on the decking. Fasten the decking on with the locator screws and take the next two pieces off. This time when you glue, you should add putty made with fibers if the tops of your shelves look uneven (check across with a straightedge) and to fill any gaps between the side panels and the shelves. Last, glue your bow pieces and set them in place. Starting at the transom, nail off your decks using 3d nails, a line along each edge on 8-inch centers. Clean up your squeeze-out but don't do any serious filling of the deck joints, and don't set the nails now.

Drilling Holes

While the epoxy is curing in your deck joints, you can drill all your holes for lines (the

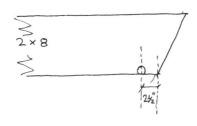

Figure 13-10. The location of the holes in the 2 x 8.

term sailors use for ropes) and for the transom drains. There are two 1½-inch holes in each deck (see Figure 1-4 for placement) for tie-up lines and fenders. Clamp scrap under the shelves as you drill to prevent splintering.

There are three holes in the transom. To drill the two 1¼-inch holes through the 2 × 8 (Figure 13-10), clamp scrap under the edge to help you get your drill started (Figure 13-11). Drill until your pilot comes through the outside and then finish the hole from outside in. Drill the 1⅛-inch drain hole through the bottom of the transom at an angle of 78 degrees; in other words, keep your drill parallel the bottom of the hull. *If you are building a skiff with no flotation tank bulkhead under the drywell, make this hole 1 inch.* Again, finish the hole from the outside.

There are two holes high in the bow for your painter (bow tie-up line). Put a ⅛-inch bit in your drill and poke the point *as high up* as you can get it under the shelf and still drill fairly square to the side panel (I slant the drill a little to get more height). The point should also be ¾ inch out from where the panel meets the bowstem. Drill holes through each side opposite one another. Now you can drill 1⅛-inch holes through from the outside, holding backing against the inside of the hull.

Use your router to round the edges of the holes through the side decks, through the 2 × 8, and the ones for the painter. You'll have to round the insides of the 2 × 8 holes by hand, as well as part of the bottom edges of the deck holes (Figure 13-12). Sand the inner edges of the painter holes.

There are two more 1⅜-inch holes low in the bow for your trailer winch line and for the line in case you need a tow home. These holes must be drilled perpendicular to the face of the bowstem but just alongside it. Since your drill has to enter the side panel at an angle, I strongly recommend you make a fixture to start your holes accurately (Figure 13-13). I also recommend using a hole saw. You'll have to drill, remove the fixture, drill some more, chisel away some wood, and then finish the hole.

Figure 13-11. *Drilling the holes in the 2 x 8, using clamped scrap to guide the start.*

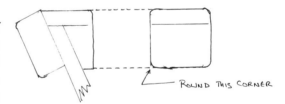

Figure 13-12. *The inner half of the bottom of the deck holes must be well-rounded.*

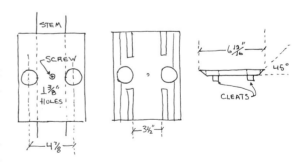

Figure 13-13. *Drilling fixture for the bow pipe holes.*

Finishing the Interior   •161

Installing the Bow Pipe

Now is a good time to install the bow pipe. Assemble the tubing and the elbows (Chapter 4) and stick the ends through the holes. Tap the bow pipe tight against the stem. Use a marking pen to mark the ends of the elbows sticking through the outside of the hull and cut them off with a hacksaw. Soak the edges of the hole thoroughly with epoxy and put the pipe back in. Put heavy fillets around the pipe, filling the area inside the U nearly level. (I put wood flour in the putty so it won't sag out underneath.) Brush on epoxy to smooth your fillet and cover the whole pipe and fillet with 6-inch, 6-ounce tape (see Figure 13-25).

On the outside of the hull, putty the sides of the holes where the pipe falls short. After the putty cures, it will take a couple more trips over the outside to get it right. You'll want to round the front edges of the holes and fill between pipe and the plywood. Grind the pipe flush if it needs it and round the inside edges with a file. Finally—important—coat the putty with epoxy.

Figure 13-14. Drilling the bow pipe holes.

Figure 13-15. Putting a fillet around the bow pipe.

Finishing the Spray Rails

The tops of your rails can be smooth if the layers match or very uneven if they don't. Planing can be a problem if the grain in the layers runs opposite ways, so you may want to use your disc or a belt sander, or even a Surform. Sand the tops of the rails and round their edges with your orbital.

They generally need a lot of filling, and I find the best way is to trowel putty all the way across with the side of my knife and then strike it off. You'll need a spotlight to make sure all voids are completely full. Epoxy them with your 2-inch roller and let the first coat cure before adding the second. A tip: the rails are hard to coat without making drips; give each coat ten minutes to run, then wipe the outer face of the rail in one long stroke with a rag.

Finishing the Side Decks

To fair the outer bevel of the side decks you'll need a freshly sharpened blade in your plane. Plane with the grain of the plywood, checking often for fairness across with a straightedge and fairness along by eye. The big danger is taking off too much; better to leave a little daylight under your straightedge and have a nice, round curve. Because of the grain direction, you'll find it's hard to plane the bow piece without chipping the edge. Suggestion: before you plane the edge, guess at how much wood you want to take off and plane the top surface back that much.

To fair the inside, run around it with a flush trimming bit in your router and finish it with your rounding-over bit. If you're too—er—thrifty (I'm groping for the right word) to buy the flush trimming bit, you can plane the plywood flush by angling your plane where the decks curve. Here again, knock the corner off before you plane to prevent splintering. Tip: bring the decks down almost flush and then round them with your router; it's now easier to plane that last little bit without gouging the shelves.

Take out the locator screws, set all the nails, and sand the decks with your orbital. Putty all the voids in the deck tops and fill the inside and outside deck seams flush. (Don't neglect the outside seams even though they will be covered with the rub rails.) Let the putty set up a little and roll epoxy onto only the tops and inner faces (you'll do the outside later). Roll on 6-inch, 6-ounce tape, leaving a scant ⅛ inch beyond the outer edge of the decks. The tape won't quite cover the inner face toward the front. Close 'nuf. Perhaps you have a triangular scrap of glass to finish the deck at the bow.

When you return to the decks after the epoxy cures, trim the glass (I use my Surform), feather and fill the seams in the tape, and roll on a final coat of epoxy. Now

Figure 13-16. Routing the inner edge of the deck.

that the putty is hard in the outer deck seams, epoxy them also. You'll owe them another coat—I'll remind you.

Making the Transom Drywell

The drywell is a box to catch water coming over the transom, which drains back out of the skiff through the holes in the 2 × 8. If you are building a skiff with a narrow motor

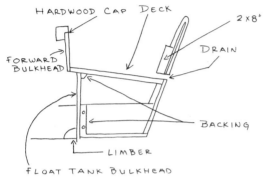

Figure 13-17. Drywell detail.

cutout, you could make the drywell the same width (Figure 2-6), or you could make it the full width of the skiff, like the one in the construction photos. In either case, you'll put the box together first and then install it.

The Bottom

The first step in building a full-width drywell is to rip the second remainder from your front side panels 18 inches wide with your saw set at 12 degrees. As you can see in Figure 13-17,

Figure 13-18. Marking the full-sized drywell pattern on the hull side—square with the transom.

this panel, which is the floor of the box, will be turned so that the *larger* face is up and its square edge is against the transom.

The best way to fit the panel is to make a full-sized pattern. First, you'll need two pieces of scrap plywood about 6 × 24 inches. Rip one edge on each piece at 23 degrees to go against the side of the hull. You'll fit these to the sides and transom at each end of the 2 × 8. You can pick up the side-to-transom angles with your bevel square and transfer them to your stock. Make the cuts and try each piece, holding it square to the 2 × 8 (Figure 13-18). When the fit is right (look in the drain holes), tack each piece to the underside of the 2 × 8. Now, mark the sides of the hull along the tops of your pieces, making sure—most important!—that the pieces stay square to the 2 × 8. You can finish your pattern by screwing a plywood ripping to both pieces, making sure they stay on the lines you drew on the hull.

Carefully remove your pattern and set it on the panel so that the side that was against the transom is now on the panel's square

Figure 13-19. Checking the opposite side.

edge. Oh, dear! The panel's too small. No matter—you can glue on a little triangle. Mark the panel and make the cuts at 23 degrees, like those on your pattern. Now, fit your panel to the hull (look in those drain holes again), and when it's right, pick up the angle between the panel at its forward edge and the hull, holding your bevel square plumb. The angles on the left and right sides should be the same; if not, recheck the panel for square against the 2 × 8. If the panel doesn't touch the hull when it's square, make a note of the width of the gap.

The Front

You should have a remainder of ½-inch plywood about 6 inches wide left over from the side of your center thwart. Rip it full width with your saw set at 12 degrees (to bevel one edge). This will be the front side of your drywell. You will nail through it and into the bottom panel. To hold the panels in position, cut two 2 × 4 blocks at 78 degrees and screw them to the floor panel (Figure 13-20). Tack the front panel to the bottom panel with two 3d nails, bevel edge to bevel edge, with the ends running wild. Use a sharp

Figure 13-20. Blocks temporarily screwed to the bottom panel support the front panel of the drywell. Note the angle cut on the ends of the blocks.

pencil to mark the edges of the floor panel on the front panel. Now's the time to add those gaps (if any) you noted above. Remove the front panel, mark it with your bevel square, and cut it. Retack it to the floor panel and fit it to the hull.

The Cap

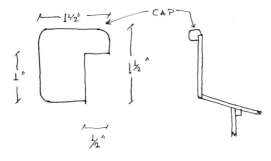

Figure 13-21. Detail of the drywell cap.

The last piece of your drywell is the cap for the front panel. I use hardwood, but any straight 2-inch stock will do. Rip a piece 2 inches longer than the panel and 1½ × 1½ inches net. Cut a rabbet in your cap stock ½ × 1 inch (Figure 13-21) and fasten the cap to the front panel with two 1¼-inch locator screws. Mark the cap along the ends of the panel and cut it. Reinstall the cap and again fit your drywell to the hull. You can now glue

A SKIFF FOR ALL SEASONS

your drywell pieces and fasten them together with more nails and screws.

Instructions for Skiffs with No Drywell Bulkheads

If you're building a skiff with no bulkhead under the drywell, you can install your drywell when the glue cures. The installation instructions are in the next chapter, where the instructions for making the bulkhead include how to put in all the parts at once.

To complete the rear of a skiff with no bulkhead, all you need to do (aside from installing the drywell) is install a 1-inch brass drain tube. Put it in the drain hole—flange

Figure 13-22. Attaching the drywell cap.

inside—and cut the tube to the angle of the rear of the transom with ³⁄₁₆ inch sticking out. Before you install the tube, seal the sides of the hole with at least two coats of epoxy. Run beads of bedding compound (use a non-polyurethane compound—see Chapter 4) around the flange and along the tube itself, and after you put it through the hull, put another bead around the outer end and shape it with your finger.

Building the Forward Flotation Tank

The flotation tank is made with a bulkhead (a vertical panel running across the hull) joined to a deck (a horizontal panel). The deck is made up of two separate panels supported by a center beam and the center beam is supported by a doubler (Figure 13-23). If you are building a skiff that has only this flotation tank, use the remaining scrap from your front side panels to make the deck, but if you are going for the locker, save them for the locker top. You can then use ¼-inch ply-

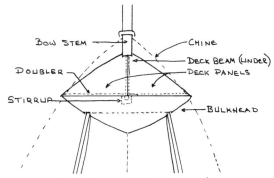

Figure 13-23. Forward flotation tank parts.

Figure 13-24. Marking the stem for the deck beam.

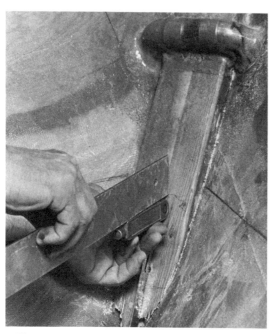

Figure 13-25. Measuring the angle for the forward end of the deck beam.

wood (even ACX is OK) for the deck since it becomes the floor of the locker, which can be less strong.

Start by ripping a piece of plywood 6 inches wide and rough cut about 3 feet long for the doubler. The doubler will sit vertical on the stringers so that its rear face is 57⅝ inches forward of the center thwart. (For skiffs without center thwarts, the measurement is 60 inches forward of Station 6.) It is good if you can cut the doubler to length so that its ends touch the hull for support (cut it by trial-and-error). Otherwise, you'll have to temporarily support it to keep it vertical. Using a second 6-inch piece across the stringers, run a straightedge forward and make a mark on the bowstem for the end of your deck beam (Figure 13-24). Cross this mark with a centerline and also draw a centerline on your doubler. Note: make the necessary allowance if the ends of your stringers are bent inwards.

You can now rip a deck beam 1½ inches wide by 2 inches deep. Cut it to length and with the right angle to fit against the stem (Figure 13-25). Make a stirrup on the doubler (Figure 13-26), drop the square end of the beam into it, and screw the other end to the stem.

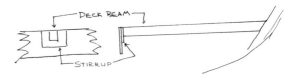

Figure 13-26. Stirrup detail.

Making Bulkhead and Deck Patterns

You're ready to make a pattern to get the shape of your bulkhead. (If you are going to make a storage locker, you will also need to read in the next chapter how to make the taller bulkhead.) When you made the pattern for the floor of the drywell, you made it to the exact shape and then traced around it. This pattern will be different, and you'll use the same method to fit all the rest of the bulkheads and decks in your skiff.

Figure 13-27. Installing the deck beam between the stirrup on the doubler and the bow stem. Note temporary support hot-glued between doubler and beam to keep the deck pattern from sagging during marking.

Make your pattern the rough shape of the bulkhead or deck but about an inch smaller. Tack the pattern in place where the bulkhead or deck will go. Now you can reach from the pattern to the hull with a marking gauge—I use a 2 × 4-inch piece of metal—and outline its shape on the pattern (Figure 13-28). Repeat this process at different points around the edge of the pattern to record the shape of the bulkhead or deck. When you place the pattern on your plywood stock, you can replace your piece of metal (or whatever you choose for a gauge) on the outlines on the pattern and mark the shape of the hull on the stock (Figure 13-29).

Make your pattern out of material as thick as your finished bulkhead or deck, or if it is thinner, shim it so that its surface is in the same plane the surface of the finished bulkhead will be in. If you mark from a thinner pattern, your marking gauge will meet the hull where it is smaller (in this skiff, at least), and you'll make your bulkhead too small. (There's another choice: if you use a ¼-inch pattern to mark a ⅜-inch bulkhead, you can use a ⅛-inch-thick marking gauge [¼ + ⅛ = ⅜]. But the end must be chisel-shaped so *only its upper surface touches the hull*).

Figure 13-28. Marking a pattern using a rectangular marking gauge.

Figure 13-29. Transferring measurements from the pattern to the stock.

Before you can saw out your bulkhead or deck you must pick up the angle your pattern makes with *each* panel the part will contact. In the case of the flotation tank bulkhead, you will measure two angles, bulkhead-to-side panel and bulkhead-to-bottom panel (let's assume both sides of the hull will make the same angles). Important: when you set your bevel square to the angle, the limbs of the square must make 90 degree angles with the pattern and with the panel (Figure 13-30).

Making the Flotation Tank (and the Locker Floor)

I think you'll now be able to screw a pattern to the doubler and pick up the shape of your bulkhead. Make your pattern for the flotation tank bulkhead the same height as the doubler, but extending down to about an inch from the bottom of the hull between the stringers. You'll want to contact each bottom panel in three places inside the stringers to get the curved shape. To record the exact shape of the keel fillet, a pointed marking gauge helps, or you can just guess and plane. (For those of you who are going to make a storage locker, this method will give you the shape of the bottom of your bulkhead; see the next chapter for how to get the top shape.) Pick up your angles, mark your stock, and cut it. Screw your finished bulkhead to the doubler.

To make a deck panel pattern, cut a curve roughly the shape of the hull. Make the pattern large enough to overhang the deck beam and the bulkhead slightly. Important!—your pattern must not sag; a temporary support can be attached with hot-glue (see Figure 13-27). Record the shape of the side panel with your gauge (a pointed

A SKIFF FOR ALL SEASONS

gauge works well at the stem). Now, *mark the hull at each point your gauge meets it.* Put your pattern on your stock and mark it (make sure your stock is as big as your pattern). Cut your stock with your saw set at the angle the pattern makes with the hull, and fit it to the hull along the marks you made. When you're happy with the fit, mark the centerline of the beam and trace underneath along the top of the bulkhead (or, for those of you making a locker, along the doubler). Make these two final cuts.

The second panel is a repeat of the first. When you've finished, round the rear edges of both deck panels with your router.

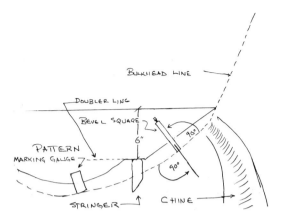

Figure 13-30. Determining the edge angles of the bulkhead.

Figure 13-31. Using a pointed gauge to mark the stem outline.

14 | Building the Rear Flotation Tank, the Forward Locker, and Finishing the Skiff

After you build your rear flotation tank and forward locker—or simply install your drywell and forward flotation tank—there are still a few odds and ends left to do. (Actually you'll find when you build a Tolman Skiff, you never really finish it—you just quit when you get tired of working on it.) The biggest item is putting on the rubrails. You'll also install the cover on the center thwart, and you'll need to put a non-skid surface on the inside of the bottom and recoat the chine. Finally, I'll give you a checklist of other things that might need attention. Perhaps you'll want to install some of the add-ons in the next chapter—most everybody wants oarlocks, for example. When your patience runs out, paint her up and go.

The Drywell Continued: Bulkhead Backing

Because you'll be able to reach only one side of your tank bulkhead, you'll need backing to hold it in place while you glue and tape it. First, you'll need to draw some lines. Square up both sides of your stringers from your limbers. Draw a second set of square lines ⅜ inch to the rear of the first lines. Use your square to draw a line on the bottom of the hull connecting the rear edges of the limbers

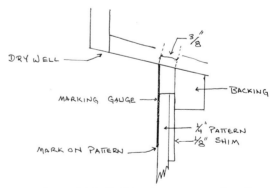

Figure 14-1. Bulkhead-to-transom detail.

Figure 14-2. Fitting the drywell. Note bulkhead backing pieces on stringers and underside of drywell.

and mark its center. Now you can cut and dry-fit (no glue) four little pieces of backing on the stringers just behind the second set of square lines.

You'll put one more piece of backing on the bottom of the drywell to catch the top of the bulkhead. Install the drywell, making sure it's seated against the transom. Run a straightedge along one of the backing pieces on each stringer up to the underside of the drywell and mark it. Remove the drywell and draw a line across the bottom through the two marks. Make sure the line is parallel to the edge of the box; you may have to adjust the backing on one of the stringers slightly to make this happen. Rip the backing for the underside of the drywell with a 12 degree angle on top so the face will be perpendicular (Figure 14-1) and dry-fit it. Now glue all the backing and install it permanently.

Extending the Drain

You'll have to extend the transom drain with a piece of 1-inch ID copper tubing passing through the flotation tank (Chapter 4). Push the tube through the drain hole until its forward end rests on the line between the limbers. Cut the rear end $\frac{3}{16}$ inch beyond the rear of the transom and at the angle of the transom. Fix the forward end of the tube so it can't move with a strap of plumber's tape (Figure 14-3). I fasten the strap with two

½-inch panhead tapping screws through washers. For now, leave the strap loose and slide the tube a little to the rear.

Making a Bulkhead Pattern

You'll need a piece of scrap plywood 15 × 67½ inches for a pattern. Even though the bulkhead will be ⅜-inch plywood, your pattern can be ¼-inch if you shim where it rests against the backing (Figure 14-1). Notch the plywood to fit over your stringers, making the notches fit exactly to the inner surfaces of the stringers and 8½ inches deep. Slide the pattern over the stringers and against the backing and cut and fit by trial and error until it roughly fits the hull. The top of the notches should seat against the tops of the stringers.

Figure 14-3. Plumber's tape screwed to the bottom holds the transom drain tube; scribing bulkhead for the drain hole.

Turn your drywell upside down and put marks at each end ⅜ inch forward of the backing; these represent the front face of your bulkhead. Put the drywell back into the hull and tack the (shimmed) pattern to the backing on the stringers. Use your marking gauge to record the shape of the hull. You'll want to contact the hull twice along one side panel, twice along the bottom outside the stringers, and so on across the hull. Last, place your marking gauge against the bottom of the drywell at each top corner of your pattern to record the height of your bulkhead.

Cutting the Bulkhead

You've used up all your remainders from the skin panels of your skiff, so you'll have to rip a 16-inch strip from a whole sheet of ⅜-inch plywood. Set your saw at 12 degrees, making the cut so that the larger face measures 16 inches. Put your pattern on the larger face of your stock and place your marking gauge on one of the last two marks you made on the pattern. Move your pattern so that the gauge is lined up with the bevelled edge of the stock. Clamp the pattern to the stock and repeat the process with your gauge at the other corner of the pattern; to get it right you may have re-align the first corner. Now you're ready to mark the shape of your bulkhead in the usual way.

I like three holes for easy access into my flotation tank, and I've found that Beckson pop-out deck plates are watertight. Of course, feel free to use any watertight hatch you

Figure 14-4. Checking the drywell bulkhead for fit.

choose. For the 8-inch center deck plate, draw an 8½-inch circle centered in the bulkhead from both directions. Center the 6½-inch circles for height but move them closer than center to the stringers. Saw out your bulkhead using a Skilsaw and a jigsaw.

Remove your drywell (I'll bet it's half worn out) and give the bulkhead its final fitting. Slide the drain pipe forward until it touches the bulkhead and tighten the plumber's tape before you trace around it (Figure 14-3). Remove the bulkhead. I'll leave it up to you how to find the center of the drain. Drill your 1⅛-inch hole and fit the drain tube with the bulkhead in place. Also, try the drywell one last time to make sure the bulkhead is letting it up come down on its marks. When the drywell is in its proper place, trace around its front side and cap and all around the forward face of the bulkhead. Ready at last.

Installing the Drywell and Bulkhead

Well, not quite. Even though the flotation tank is watertight, I'm very fussy about epoxying *all* surfaces. Remove the pieces and roll on as much epoxy as you can in one coat on the inner face of the bulkhead and the underside of the drywell. Do the part of the drywell bottom forward of the backing and the underside of the hardwood cap while they're still easy to get at. Get a jump on all the end grain by wiping your roller out on it. Have you remembered to coat the edges of the deck plate holes?

Remove the drain pipe and soak the inside of the transom hole with epoxy. Put it back and clamp it tightly in place with the plumber's tape.

You will drive one screw from each side through the side panel into the hardwood cap on the front panel of the drywell. Drill pilot holes from the inside to locate these screws. As usual, wipe down the hull. It's glue time, and from here on you should work continuously until the drywell and bulkhead are installed and the taping is complete.

Coat the floor of the drywell where it will contact the 2 × 8 and the edges that go against the hull with lots of fiber putty. Install the drywell and drive seven evenly spaced 1⅝-inch screws up through the floor into the 2 × 8 (but not through the drains!). Drill for and drive screws through the outside of the hull into the hardwood cap. Put large fillets on either side of the drain tube and around its transom end, and cover it with 6-inch, 6-ounce tape, lapping the tape onto the transom. Hold the fillets and tape back about ⅜ inch from the inner end of the tube. Glue up the bulkhead, install it, and nail it with enough 3d nails to hold it against the backing.

Figure 14-5. Fiberglassing the drain tube.

You've now got a mile of fillet and tape to run. Divide it into three parts: the bulkhead, the drywell and the transom. Do both the fillets and the taping together in each part but don't epoxy the panels until all the fillet and taping are finished. All tape is 4-inch, 6-ounce. Some joints aren't taped; make sure they are filled with putty, however. Set your nails and putty the heads.

The Bulkhead

Tape against the hull but not to the bottom of the drywell. Notch the ends of pieces of tape and run them through the limbers. Run a single piece of tape around the stringers (Figure 14-6). Tape right across the drain hole.

Figure 14-6. Taping around the stringers.

The Drywell

The tape goes up both sides of the front panel and around the edge of the floor, but not up the 2 × 8. Again, tape across the drain holes.

The Transom

You will run fillets on the tops of the corner braces but not tape them, and there are two little fillets at the inside corners of the motor cutout. Wet out the top of the transom and run the tape continuous from one deck to the other, slashing it twice at each inside and outside corner so it will lie flat. Don't forget to paint your corner brace fillets with epoxy.

Finishing

Now you can wet out the bulkhead and the drywell floor with your 3-inch roller. Check the transom for drips. This might be a good time to roll that second coat of epoxy on the outside deck joint. When you scrape the epoxy out of your roller, use it on the insides of the drywell drain holes, the holes through the side decks, and the painter holes.

Building the Front Storage Locker: The Bulkhead

In Chapter 13 I described how to make the doubler, deck beam, and deck panels, which will be the floor of your locker. If you were going to make a storage locker, you made a pattern with the shape of the bottom of the hull and lower sides marked on it, but you didn't make the short bulkhead. You should now have your locker floor tacked together in the hull with the pattern fastened to the doubler with locator screws. To get the shape of the taller bulkhead, you've got to make what I call a grasshopper (although it isn't green and has only two legs)—a 22 × 31½-inch panel braced to stand perpendicular to the stringers (Figure 14-7).

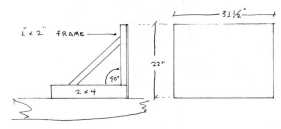

Figure 14-7. Grasshopper.

Stand the grasshopper on the stringers, pushed against your pattern. Note: your pattern must be the thickness of the bulkhead—⅜ inch—or it should be shimmed so its rear face is ⅜ inch from the doubler. Lay a straightedge along the top forward edge of the grasshopper and mark on both sides where it meets the hull. Mark a center point

Figure 14-8. Measuring from the centerline on the grasshopper to the hull.

on the top of the grasshopper by squaring up from the centerline of the locker floor. Measure from this center point the distance in each direction to the marks on the hull.

You need one more piece of information to get the shape of your bulkhead. Extend the centerline of the deck to the rear of your pattern. Measure the distance to the hull in each direction. You should also mark these points on the hull. Draw lines between the upper and lower marks on the hull to mark the location of the rear edge of the bulkhead. You can now draw the bulkhead on a sheet of plywood using your pattern and these two sets of measurements.

Cut your bulkhead. Don't forget to make your cuts with your saw set to the proper angles (see Chapter 13). Fit your bulkhead to the hull so that it lies against the doubler and along the lines you drew on the side panels. You can now mark your bulkhead at the top points on the sides of the hull, draw a line and make the top cut. For the faint-of-heart, a more cautious approach calls for putting the marks, say, 1 inch down, then cutting the sides and bottom, which are then fit to the hull. When the fit is right, pick up the marks from the hull and saw the top edge.

Building the Front Storage Locker: Framing the Deck

Fasten your bulkhead to the doubler with two locator screws. It is very important at this point to keep the bulkhead plumb and straight. You can keep it on the marks you made

Figure 14-9. Plumbing and nailing the forward bulkhead.

on the hull with 3d nails tacked to the hull (Figure 14-9). Fasten a temporary strong back (Figure 14-10) to the bulkhead 6 or so inches below the top to keep the plywood straight.

Note the names of the parts of the framing in Figure 14-10 so you'll know what I'm talking about. Begin laying out your hatch opening by marking the top edge of the bulkhead 1 foot each side of center. These mark the centers of the rear ends of the deck beams, and you need to find where the front beam centers meet the hull. First, find the height *on each side of the hull* by laying a straightedge across your grasshopper and the top of the bulkhead. Next, square forward to the hull from your beam center mark on the bulkhead. You need this point (point A) *on one side of the hull only.*

Rip out the stock for your deck beams. You'll notice that the rabbet (notch) in the coaming around the inside of the hatch opening is the same size as the rabbet in the deck beams; you can save time by sawing all your stock out at once. *Make sure the rabbets are accurate.*

To cut the first beam, lay a piece of 2 × 2 running from the beam center mark on the bulkhead to point A on the hull. Record the

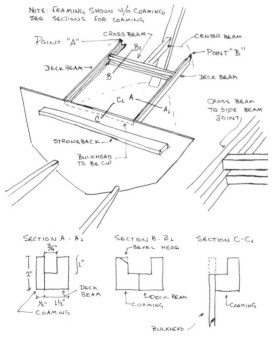

Figure 14-10. Front storage locker detail.

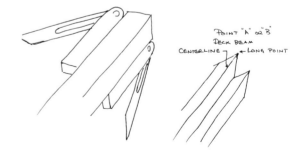

Figure 14-11. Measuring the angles for the deckbeam-to-hull fit.

A Skiff for all Seasons

Figure 14-12. Fastening the hatch framing in position.

beam length to the inside of the bulkhead and measure the two angles with your bevel square (Figure 14-11). First cut the angle on the end of the beam and fit it to the hull, then cut the beam to length. Remember, measure the beam's length along its centerline. Fasten the beam in place with two locator screws at the rear and one at the front (never mind if the front locator screw goes through the hull).

Square across the hull from the rabbet in beam one with the 2-foot limb of your framing square and mark point B. Now you can cut beam two. Cut the cross beam and put it in place between the beams as you fit beam two to the hull. When the fit is right, remove both beams and screw the cross beam in place with two screws in each end. Make sure the crossbeam centerline is 24 inches *from the rear of the bulkhead.*

Figure 14-13. Checking that the tops of the deckbeams, centerbeam, crossbeam, and the bulkhead are all fair across.

Building the Rear Flotation Tank, the Forward Locker, and Finishing the Skiff • 181

Put the three beams back in the hull as a unit and fasten beam two. Check the hatch opening for squareness. Cut and install the center beam. Important: as you fit this beam and the following four coaming pieces, align their top edges with a straightedge laid across beams one and two. Cut first the front and rear coaming pieces and then the side pieces and install them all with two locator screws each. Don't cut the notch in the top of the bulkhead yet.

Front Storage Locker: Deck and Hatch Cover

Now that your framing is complete, you can make a pattern and fit your deck just as you did the locker floor. Make sure your deck panels don't ride up the hull; when you remove one, does the other want to slide over the centerline? Plane the rear edges of your panels perfectly flush with the bulkhead and round them with your router. You can now remove the panels and cut the notch in the top edge of the bulkhead at the hatch.

To mark the hatch opening, replace both panels. Important: when you remove one panel, always leave the other in place on the deck so your panels won't shift. Tack panel one with three 3d nails and remove panel two. You can pick up the two edges of your opening by squaring from the beam centers and from the crossbeam. I find the inner corner accurately by recording the two distances to the rabbets on a stick poked underneath the panel and transferring these distances to the top of the panel.

Replace panel two and tack it before you remove panel one to cut it. Mark panel two and replace panel one. Remove panel two and cut it. Plane the panels as necessary to fit the framing, then round their edges around the hatch.

To make the hatch cover, glue the two cut-out pieces together, centerline to centerline, and tape the bottom-side seam with 4-inch, 6-ounce tape. Note: if this joint makes you nervous, groove it with a table saw or router and put in a spline (Figure 14-14). Plane this panel to fit the hatch opening with ⅛ inch clearance on three sides when the fourth is flush with the bulkhead. Tip: use six ⅛-inch shims to get the proper spacing. Round the corners and make and install the ⅞-inch lip (Figure 14-14) around the edge. Finger grooves cut with a router are a nice touch.

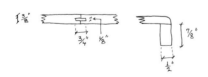

Figure 14-14. Hatch cover detail.

Installing the Storage Locker

You're now ready to take the whole locker apart and epoxy the inside surfaces. *Don't epoxy the surfaces on the framing that will be glued together later.* It's best to let the epoxy cure before you begin installation.

Put in the locker floor and front bulkhead. Fill any cracks there may be between the locker floor and the hull. Run fillets around the floor and tape it to the bulkhead and hull. Fill and tape the center seam. Run fillet inside of the bulkhead and tape it, making sure the bulkhead is on its line. Hold it in place with a 3d nail or two tacked to the hull if necessary. Epoxy the floor.

Now you can glue in the framing and deck. As usual, fill the edges before you do the fillet. Tape the edges of the deck and bulkhead and put 6-ounce cloth on the deck, wrapping it over the edges of the hatch opening. Tip: it is easiest to put three separate triangles of cloth on the deck. Finally, put cloth on the hatch cover and epoxy the bulkhead.

Figure 14-15. Taping around the hatch opening.

Putting on the Rubrails

The rubrails can either be hardwood or UHMW (Chapter 4). Both are ¾-inch stock ripped 1½ inches wide and are fastened with #10 × 2-inch stainless screws. The wood rails are fastened on 12-inch centers, but because the bedding compound doesn't stick to UHMW, these rails must be fastened on 6-inch centers. Mark *both* faces of the rails for your screw centers but don't predrill them. Each rail requires a 10- and a 12-foot piece of hardwood, but since UHMW comes only in 10-foot sheets, you must cut five 10-foot pieces of stock. Round the edges of the stock with your router.

If your rails are hardwood, start at the bow with a 12-foot piece. With a hand saw, cut the rail (either wood or UHMW) at the bow with an angle of 60 degrees on the ¾-inch side and the deck-to-stem angle on the 1½-inch side. With your power saw, cut the joint where the pieces of rail join with your saw set at 30 degrees, making the forward piece lap over the rear piece. Run a bead of bedding compound (I use black Sikaflex) along the front edge and the top of the face that will lie against the hull, as well as a dab on all the screw centers. Don't put bedding compound on the joint where the rails join yet.

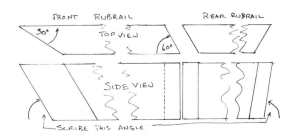

Figure 14-16. Rubrail detail.

Installing the rail is a two-person job, and wooden rails behave a little differently than UHMW rails do.

Installing Wooden Rails

Drill the holes with a few degrees of slant so that the ends of the screws won't break through the deck, and countersink the screw heads well below the surface. The bedding compound makes the rail slide down the hull, and bending the rail edgeways as well as around the hull also drags it down. Always drill your holes with the edge of the rail *slightly above the deck*—hold the rail a full ⅛ inch high for the first hole and ¹⁄₁₆ inch thereafter, leaving the rail flush or slightly raised after you drive the screws. The rail must also twist, and it helps to force the bottom in with a bar clamp as you go along. If your rail drops below the deck, remove the screw, back up 6 inches and drive another screw with the rail held higher. Chances are you can now replace the first screw.

Installing UHMW Rails

UHMW is much more flexible. Start your rail ¹⁄₁₆ inch high and you won't need clamping. When you get around the bend, hold the rail only the slightest bit above deck height. Countersink the screw heads just below the surface.

When you finish the first piece of rail (of either material), dry-fit the second, recutting the joint if necessary. Scribe the rear end to the transom angle and cut it to end where the rounded corner begins. Set your saw at 30 degrees, making the side against the hull the longer one. Put bedding compound on the face of the joint before you install the rear piece of rail.

Figure 14-17. Keeping the rail slightly high while installing screws.

Your bedding compound will squeeze out at the deck joint. Pick up the surplus with your putty knife and fill any voids. *Let the compound harden*. Putty the screw heads (wood rails only). If you use apitong, as I do, microballons match well. If you use oak or ash, use wood flour. Run a continuous bead of bedding compound under the rails, sames as you did along the edges of the bottom strakes. The next day you can scrape the wood or UHMW flush with the deck and remove the excess compound at the same time. Scraping is slow; you can plane and then scrape, but be *very* careful. Let the compound harden another day or two and then sand the rails with your orbital. I wouldn't epoxy the rails, but suit yourself (see Painting, page 187).

Odds and Ends

If you haven't done so already, you should feather all your tape around the bow locker (or flotation tank), along the chine, where the center thwart meets the hull, and around the drywell and transom. The amount you fill is up to you, but I think it improves the looks of your skiff greatly to give all tape edges one shot of putty with your 1-inch knife. Then sand and recoat all the tape, using a brush and small roller together. Note: epoxy the full width of the tape but *don't recoat the floor or front deck yet*. Perhaps hard-to-coat areas, like the top of the transom, will need yet another coat. Do the edges of the front hatch cover (but not the top), inside the drywell, and the front and rear bulkheads.

You should check your holes through the side decks and sand and recoat them if necessary. The drywell drains should be filed smooth and puttied (use your finger) and epoxied thoroughly so they won't leak into the rear flotation tank. Are the bow holes well-coated? With a mirror and light make sure your drain tube is sealed against the rear of the rear flotation bulkhead. Check the channels around the hatch in the forward storage locker—are the joints well-filled and sealed?

Mounting Covers and Deck Plates

You can mount the front locker hatch cover, the center thwart cover, and the deck plates in the rear flotation tank bulkhead before or after you paint. Use clear silicone for bedding.

For the front locker hatch, cut 22 inches from a 6-foot stick of 1½-inch stainless piano hinge. I use ⅜-inch panhead stainless screws, but use flatheads if you want. Give each hole a shot of silicone before driving the screw. If you want, mount a friction catch under the lid (Chapter 4). Use scrap UHMW to make lid bumpers to protect the deck (Figure 14-18).

Figure 14-18. UHMW scraps screwed to the inside of the shelf provide bumpers for the opened hatch.

Put the remainder of the piano hinge on the underside of the thwart lid and on the thwart. The lid should be centered on the thwart in both directions. I mount the hinge on the forward side of the thwart. If your piano hinge has holes drilled opposite (not offset), you must use flathead (instead of panhead) screws. Buy 2 feet of non-rusting light chain (called brailer chain in my local chandlery) to keep the lid from opening too far and tearing out the hinge. You may want a friction catch or two, particularly if the lid is warped.

Mount the Beckson deck plates in the rear bulkhead with #8 stainless panhead screws. I put a ring of caulk under the plate frame *and* a bead around the frame after it is installed to make sure. Install the brass drain tube insert (1 inch O.D.) using lots of bedding compound (see Chapter 4, Materials).

Putting Sand on the Bottom and Deck

Putting sand in the final coat of resin on the skiff's inner bottom and foredeck (whether on the flotation tank or the storage locker) is very important, not only for non-skid but

Figure 14-19. Standing on the stringers to apply sand to the bottom.

for the tremendous durability it gives as well. (Don't put sand in the paint—I don't care how Granddad did it!) Use 20-grit sand-blasting sand, which you should be able to buy at your local tool rental or auto supply. A number ten can full should be enough. You'll need a smaller can and a flour sifter or other fine screen to spread the sand as you pour it. If you want to do a fancy job, mask the edges of the floor and deck with tape.

Do the floor in 3-foot sections, starting at the foredeck (high or low). Use your big roller to roll on a very heavy coat of epoxy. You'll need your brush to get the epoxy close along the uphill side of the stringers. Shake on sand until the surface just starts to turn white. Shake on plenty—you can remove the excess. Work your way toward the rear, standing on the stringers when necessary. The next day you can brush the white areas lightly with a wire brush and vacuum up the loose sand.

Painting

(Note: if you want to row your skiff, you should put the oarlock blocks on before you paint. See Chapter 15.)

Here are a few painting suggestions you may find helpful. Your skiff will dry faster outside, but if you paint inside, rigging a fan to blow down into the hull helps a lot. Painting is easier if you can raise the skiff—preferably on two beams across four sawhorses. You can lift it with loops of line through the painter holes and the drywell drains.

Two coats of paint are a minimum, but putting on a coat of primer first is best. If you primed the outside when the hull was upside down, you'll want to prime the side decks and the inside as well. Before you begin, by all means wash the inside thoroughly. The sand will lap up a lot of primer, but do a thorough job—it will save paint on the following coats.

Most people paint the hull one color and the side decks and spray rails another. If you decide to do this, paint the side decks first. If you have wooden rails and want to finish them natural, I suggest mixing pine tar, linseed oil, and turpentine in equal amounts, heating the mixture, and brushing it on. If you're building a yacht and must varnish, they tell me to epoxy first for long varnish life. Choose a varnish that contains a UV filter (read the label) because ultraviolet light breaks down epoxy.

Next, apply the first coat of paint on the inside of the hull and on the topsides (upper hull). Lap the paint a bit onto the spray rails and down over the fiberglass line. Paint the *underside* of the spray rails, but not their tops or faces. Don't paint the bottom of the hull yet unless, of course, you want it the same color as the topsides.

Put a second coat on the side decks. Repaint the inside and the topsides. Now you can give the tops and outer faces of the spray rails two coats for your contrasting trim color.

At this time, you can also put a different color on the bottom, and if your hand is steady, you should be able to paint the fiberglass line without masking. If your skiff is going to stay in salt water, you'll want bottom paint. The bottom fiberglass line should remain above the waterline when the skiff is moored unless you do something wild like hanging two 50s on the transom. If you want a true (i.e., level) waterline, you're on your own.

15 | Add-on Features for Your Skiff

Once you complete the basic skiff, there are any number of features you can add. Of course I can't cover all of them, but I'll describe a few of the most popular ones. You may want to launch your skiff and then add features as you need them—or can afford them. In general, if you add anything that is glued on, scrape the paint down to the epoxy first. If you add hardware, bed it in clear silicone, and if you think you may want to remove it later, put silicone only in the holes for the fasteners. Although strictly speaking it doesn't matter, I encourage you to make all add-ons out of good material (although here you may want to compromise by using ACX plywood, instead of marine), and to saturate all surfaces with epoxy.

Oarlock Sockets

For their size, Tolman Skiffs row surprisingly well, although I'll admit you'll have trouble against the wind. Rowing is handy in shallow water, where you might otherwise hit your prop, it's fun to float rivers using oars alone, and you may be able to rescue yourself if your motor quits. You'll need 10-foot oars, which will require 2¼-inch oarlocks (I recommend bronze only) with sockets elevated on blocks so the oars clear the side decks. If you're going to steer your skiff with a tiller on the outboard, the oarlocks should be mounted 9 inches behind the center thwart. If you steer from a center console, you'll have to mount the oarlocks about 2 feet behind the console so your oars will clear it.

Make your blocks out of hardwood and drill the holes for the oarlock sockets perpendicular to the angled top face (Figure 15-1). Drill the holes all the way through the shelves to let the water drain and epoxy them thoroughly. It's easier to mount the

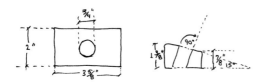

Figure 15-1. Oarlock mounting block detail.

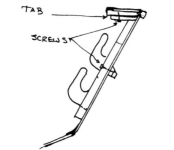

Figure 15-2. Cactus rack detail.

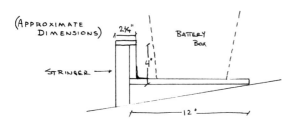

Figure 15-3. Battery box platform.

blocks, paint your skiff, and then put in the sockets.

Oar Holders

You'll need some way to secure your oars so that they won't rattle around in rough weather and when you trailer your skiff. I like both oars side-by-side on one side of the skiff, where they make a shelf to set things or can even be used for a seat. I make two holders lined with strips of inner tube to protect the oars, one on the center thwart and one on the rear framing, and keep the oars in place with shock cord. At up to $85 apiece, oars are a hot item to steal in some marinas. To hang on to them, I suggest drilling holes in the blades and the front panel of the dry-well and running a cable-type lock through them.

Cactus Racks

I make general purpose racks that have been used for oars, fishing rods, and—believe it or not—cross country skis by cutting ⅜-inch or, better yet, ½-inch plywood into cactus shapes and fastening them to the rear framing and to added framing forward. By thinning this extra framing to 1¼ inches you can fasten it through into the spray rail with a 2-inch stainless screw, and by adding a tab to the top you can screw into the shelf (Figure 15-2). This makes the racks easily removable.

Battery Box Platform

Increasingly these days outboard skiffs have electrical systems. Although I think it's more practical to buy a battery box than to build one, I like to make a platform for the box to keep it from sliding around. The platform should be sized for the particular box you buy and big enough to mount the loops and straps that come with it (Figure 15-3). You'll have to plane the outer edge to fit the changing angle of the hull. Give the platform two coats of epoxy and fasten it to the stringers with two 1½-inch #8 stainless screws and finishing washers. Note: *finishing washers*, which come in different sizes, *should be used with all screws that aren't countersunk and puttied.* Don't forget the silicone.

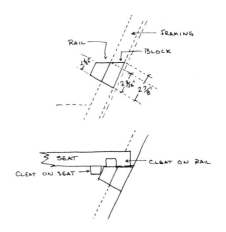

Side Rails for Extra Seats

Some owners want bench seats in addition to the center thwart. One way to make them so that they're easily removable is to install permanent rails along the side of the hull (Figure 15-4) and then lay a plank, such as a 2 × 10, across. You can put cleats on the top of the rails to keep the plank from sliding forward and back and cleats on the bottom of plank to keep it from sliding endways; scrap UHMW is good for this.

Figure 15-4. Seat support-rail detail.

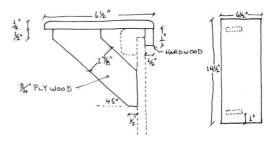

Movable Driver's Seat

Figure 15-5. Moveable driver's seat detail.

Warning: you should be very careful when driving a Tolman Skiff sitting down because the high bow limits your visibility. Always stand when you're accelerating from non-planing to planing speed because visibility is particularly limited as the hull squats. (Ask the man who recently ran over an aluminum boat here.) Move your head from side to side or steer a slightly winding course to eliminate the blind spot.

If you are planning to steer with a tiller, you might like a small movable—and removable—seat that hangs on the front of the drywell (Figure 15-5). You haven't lived until you've trolled for king salmon on a fine spring day, sitting on this seat and running your kicker. The cover of the tilted-up main motor makes a perfect backrest, and a 5-gallon pail is just right for a footrest.

Storage Box/Seat

This storage box/seat stands on the stringers and can be mounted anywhere between the center thwart and the drywell. If you use it as a driver's seat in a tiller-steered skiff,

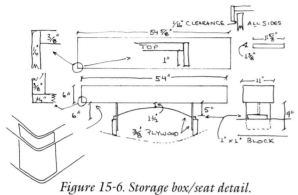

Figure 15-6. Storage box/seat detail.

you'll probably want a tiller extension to make steering easier when you're standing. This seat makes a perfect place to store your shotgun when you're duck hunting (remember: it's illegal to shoot from a moving motorboat). When I'm in brown bear country, I keep some strong medicine in mine, along with my compass and navigation charts. Thick carpet makes the inside nice.

Notice that the drawing (Figure 15-6) calls for fastening thin plywood to thick, a handy principal to remember when you're designing anything made of plywood. Also notice the plywood is only as thick as it has to be—weight matters. Make sure you put patches of tape on the corners of the lid and box as shown—the joints will certainly crack if you don't. Actually, the lid never comes off while you're at sea but only when you hit bumps trailering the skiff.

Seat Platforms

More and more owners are equipping their skiffs with pedestal seats. Because these seats are tall and their bases small, they require very stout mounting platforms, well anchored to the hull. For seats mounted between the stringers, such as those used with center steering consoles, I use two layers of ¾-inch plywood notched at the ends so that 2-inch #10 stainless screws through finishing washers will be long enough to fasten them to the stringers (Figure 15-7).

For seats mounted outside the stringers, you will need a cleat fastened to the side of the skiff (Figure 15-8). Since this cleat has to be very strongly attached, glue it permanently to the side of the hull. You can make the platform itself semi-detachable—you never know when you or a future owner might want to change the seating arrangements—by screwing it, but not gluing it, to the cleat and the stringer.

Here's how to screw these cleats to the hull without driving the screws from the outside in, which of course would require puttying and re-epoxying—and perhaps repainting.

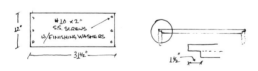

Figure 15-7. Seat platform between the stringers.

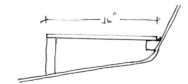

Figure 15-8. Seat platform outboard of the stringers.

Using your Fuller bit for 2½-inch screws, drill a hole through the cleat so that the drill point sticks through not quite enough to fully penetrate a piece of ⅜-inch plywood. (You can check this by holding a piece of ⅜-inch scrap next to the bit.) Mark the depth of the hole by wrapping a piece of masking tape around the countersink. The tape on your drill will show you how deep to drill the next hole. When you glue the cleat to the hull, take special pains to rough the surface thoroughly and clean it. Give the top edge of the cleat a fillet and tape it to the hull.

Floorboards

Floorboards, as distinct from decks, are removable and are not waterproof; that is, incoming water that lands on them runs through or around them into the bilge. Let me say at the beginning that I don't like floorboards. They add expense and weight. Fish guts get under them with predictable consequences. And I like the stringers exposed to keep gear from sliding around and to brace my heels against when I gaff those big halibut. But lots of owners like 'em. . . . (For a fuller discussion of decks and floorboards see Chapter 5.)

It seems like there are two basic ways to go: either with slats or with solid panels. I never happened to have built any with slats, but I will offer one piece of general advice: make the slats, which I assume will run across the skiff, into panels by fastening them to slats running at right angles to them. Panels, whether solid or slatted, will have to be supported at their outside edges either by feet resting on the floor of the hull or by cleats fastened to the hull in the manner of the pedestal seat platforms above. Roughly 1½ feet forward of the center thwart the floorboards can rest on the bottom of the hull, but they must be fitted accurately to the ever-changing angle of the bottom.

To take the measurements for a floorboard panel forward of the center thwart, here's a simpler method than making a full-sized pattern. You'll need a piece of ⅜-inch plywood (assuming your floorboard will be ⅜ inch thick) 31½ × 30 (or so) inches. Draw a centerline and lay off 6-inch points as shown in Figure 15-9. Fasten the plywood temporarily to the stringers. Now you can take measurements to the hull left and right from each of these 6-inch points. Your measurements should be taken at an exact right angle to the centerline with a non-sagging ruler, and when you need to you can move your panel to the rear a multiple of 6 inches and measure the rest. You can then draw a centerline and lay off 6-inch intervals on your floorboard stock and transfer the measurements.

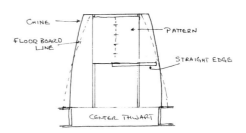

Figure 15-9. Measuring from the centerline to determine the floorboard outline.

Here are some final suggestions on floorboards. Epoxy all surfaces to keep them from absorbing water and becoming heavy, and spread sand on the tops for a non-skid surface. Make the floorboards out of ¾-inch stock to provide strength for through-bolting pedestal seats. And an important safety consideration: even though you may have a bilge pump, make a large enough section at the transom easily removable so you can bail efficiently by hand.

Decks

I make decks out of ½-inch plywood and fit them tight to the sides of the hull so that they need neither feet nor cleats to support them. I put in a spine of plywood glued to the keel to take out the flex, and I join the individual panels with gussets underneath (Figure 15-10). They are of course given a fillet and taped to the hull, and you know me well enough now to know I epoxy the underside. I spread sand on the tops for non-skid. In case there's damage to the hull or deck, I cut limbers and provide some sort of inspection plate or drain to remove possible water. Sealed decks must be vented, the same as fuel tanks, or the inside air heated by the sun will blow them apart.

If you build a deck in a skiff with a center thwart, you'll have to install drains to let water pass through it to the rear of the skiff. They should be at least 2 inch ID. I use copper pipe, but if you use plastic, seal them with bedding compound because the plastic expands and contracts a lot and will break loose from rigid epoxy. Drains are a potential trouble spot; for a skiff with decks, knees would be better for the center bracing.

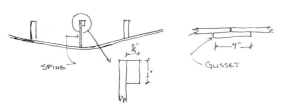

Figure 15-10. Keel spine and panel-joint gussets for decks.

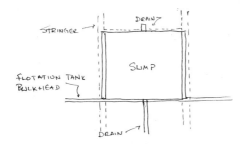

Figure 15-11. Sump detail for a decked skiff with a transom flotation tank.

To reach transom drains (there should be one at each side) when the drywell goes all the way across the hull and there is no bulkhead underneath, I put in 6-inch deck plates for access in the floor of the drywell (Figure 15-12). If there is a bulkhead, I put in the usual extended drain and leave out a section of deck to create a sump. I put in a second drain to handle possible water from under the deck. The sump is then covered by a removable plate.

By the way, although I've never built a skiff without a drywell, I question the need for a it in a decked skiff since the deck self-bails while the boat is under power. I notice some commercially built boats have no dry-

A SKIFF FOR ALL SEASONS

Figure 15-12. Deck plate for access to drywell. Note drain in transom.

wells, while others have such small ones that they wouldn't handle much water.

Steering Consoles

A console can vary from a simple L-shaped bracket coming out from the side deck and going down to the stringer to an elaborate center-mounted cabinet with a windshield, which could even support a soft top. I'll describe just one popular console (Figure 15-14), which you can build as-is or modify. You may want to change the height. As designed, the top of the windshield is eye level for a person of average height standing on the floor of the hull. In nice weather you can look over or through the windshield, and when the spray starts to fly you can duck

Figure 15-13. A side console. The panel clamped to the shelf is for engine controls. Note also the cleat on the hull for a seat platform and the side rails to support rear seating.

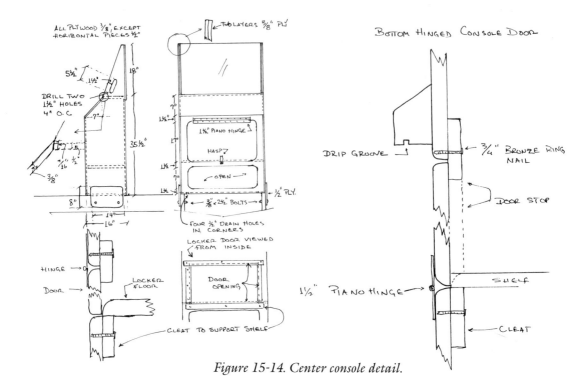

Figure 15-14. Center console detail.

down behind it. But for safety a windshield should never be so high that you can't look *over* it if your vision is partly blocked by dirt, dried salt, or drops of water.

You may want to vary the relative sizes of the two storage areas, put doors on each, and so on. As is they are designed to make it easy to install your steering, gauges, and electronics in the upper area, but perhaps you will need more space below—to install a gas tank, for example.

Take special note of the locker door construction. You should be able to cut the opening neatly enough with your jigsaw to be able to use the piece removed for your door. A tip from Mary, our locker-maker: work your jigsaw blade through the panel on the hinge side so that the piano hinge will cover your—er—less-than-perfect workmanship. You can hinge the door top or bottom, but if the latter, you will have to install an "eave" to divert water. Note the drip groove sawed into its bottom side. For easy construction, nail the ⅜-inch door stop to the ⅜-inch console face with ¾-inch bronze ringshank nails (Jamestown Supply). Since these nails don't rust, they need only to be set flush.

I strongly recommend mar-resistant ³⁄₁₆-inch Lexan for a windshield even though it's very expensive and for some reason you can't buy it tinted. If you're considering Plexiglas, use plywood instead—that's what Plexiglas will look like after one season any-

A Skiff for all Seasons

Figure 15-15. Another net skiff transom configuration.
Note binboards and forward towing bitt.

way, and the plywood is cheaper. Drill the screw holes in the Lexan slightly bigger than the outside diameter of the screws. Bed the Lexan in silicone and fasten it to the frame with 1¼-inch stainless screws spaced 3 inches on center. If you boat on saltwater, avoid wiping your windshield—salt crystals scratch even mar-resistant Lexan. Use Rain-X instead, a product developed for aircraft windshields that causes the water to bead and run off.

Net Skiffs

Above all, commercial fisherman are independent minded, and no two of the many net skiffs I've built have been quite the same. It's likely that if you are going make a net skiff from a Tolman Skiff hull, you know what you want, but here are some ideas that have worked out—and some that haven't. While these skiffs have all been built for gillnetting salmon and herring in Alaska, perhaps some of the features, such as bulkheads, binboards, towing bitts, and so on, would be useful in other parts of the country as well.

Transoms

Generally—but not always—net skiffs have offset motors to provide room to set nets over the stern. Usually with this set-up there's a 4- × 4-inch towing bit centered on the transom, which also keeps the net from snagging the motor. The top 12 inches of the bitt is round and sheathed with 3-inch ABS pipe for durability. It is important to tape the bitt to the bottom of the hull with several layers of heavy tape to keep it from pulling loose.

Drywells

Drywells should always be braced only to the transom—never to the stringers—so they can flex. You can increase freeboard at the stern by making the drywell as high as the gunwales. It must then extend forward enough to give space to work the tiller. Some fishermen like a socket on the forward corner of the drywell made of heavily fiberglassed ABS pipe. An oar stuck in the socket makes a fairlead to guide the net.

Bulkheads and Binboards

Net skiffs usually have a pair of bulkheads or binboards (or one of each) to make a fish pen, usually 5 feet long from Station 6 toward the rear. Bulkheads are at least 22½ inches high and made of ⅜-inch plywood capped, like the front panel of the drywell, with a piece of hardwood. Binboards are made of 2 × 12s stacked two high.

If a skiff has one bulkhead at Station 6, it won't need further center bracing (see Figure 2-2). Put in a piece of framing on edge as if for a knee, fasten the bulkhead to it, and tape it to the hull. If a skiff has only binboards, it will need two sets of knees, one at each set of binboards. A second piece of framing on the opposite side of the binboards keeps them in place.

Inboard Towing Bits

Some fishermen prefer to tow from forward of the transom for better steering control. A removable 4 × 4 bitt runs through a double-thick ¾-inch plywood web on the back of the upper rear binboard and is held at the bottom by a 2 × 8 running between the stringers. The 2 × 8 is mortised to receive the end of the bitt.

Gunwales

Nets dragged down by a running tide (and lots of fish) pull hard, and skiff builders have tried various methods of making them slide easily over the gunwales. I have made half-round gunwales by molding foam in split sections of 5-inch pipe, but these are very labor intensive to build. They not only need hardwood around the outer edge for strength but solid wood in the way of all the holes for fairleads and oarlocks.

You can get nearly the same results quicker and cheaper by capping the outer corners of the gunwales with two half-round (actually slightly oval) pieces of UHMW. I make these by ripping the ¾-inch UHMW 1⅝-inches wide and routing the edges with a ¾-inch rounding-over bit. This leaves a small flat through which to drive the screws. I use 2-inch ABS pipe stuck through holes in the side decks for fairleads, bevelling the ends to jam against the hull. (Salmon set-net highliners tell me nets pull easiest over aluminum rollers 3 feet wide or so with built-in fairleads. They are shifted from one gunwale to the other.)

Inverted Spray Rails

Fisherman complain that as they pull the nets, corks and fish noses bind under the spray rails. I build the rails with the bevelled side down to remedy this.

Inside Rails

Many fishermen put their fish in brailer bags (large net bags with drawstrings) to unload them efficiently. I make rails to tie the bags to just below the shelves by gluing on 2 × 6 blocks every 3 feet or so and drilling them for ½-inch aluminum rod.

Trimming the Bow

The bows of net skiffs were often splintered against the sterns of the boats that towed them or damaged because fishermen held their skiffs bow-on under power against the sides of large vessels to transfer crew. I solve this problem by sawing about 4 inches in length off the bow, making the cut plumb. I then score the back of the UHMW bow-stem strip and wrap it around onto this flat nose.

A Final Word . . .

Here's a short user's guide for your Tolman Skiff. Fix the little things before they become big things. Keep the epoxy seal intact everywhere—particularly below the waterline, and keep the epoxy painted. Run your skiff at speeds that match the sea conditions and stay away from rocky beaches. If you follow these simple rules, you and your skiff should have a long and happy association. See you on the bay.

Appendix: Tool and Supply Sources

Drills and Countersinks

W.L. Fuller Incorporated
P.O. Box 8767
7 Cypress Street
Warwick, RI 02888
401-467-2900

Fastenings and Boatbuilding Supplies

Jamestown Distributors
28 Narragansett Avenue
P.O. Box 348
Jamestown, RI 02835
1-800-423-0030

Plastic Rails (UHMW)

Wesbrook Marine
5109 Shilsole Avenue, NW
Seattle, WA 98107
206-789-3985

Resin and Fiberglass

Gougeon Brothers Incorporated
P.O. Box X908
Bay City, MI 48707
517-684-7286

System Three Resins
P.O. Box 70436
Seattle, WA 98107
1-800-333-5514

Tools

Harbor Freight Tools
3491 Mission Oaks Boulevard
P.O. Box 6010
Camarillo, CA 93011
1-800-423-2567

Northern Hydraulics
P.O. Box 1499
Burnsville, MN 55337
1-800-533-5545

Seven Corners Ace Hardware Incorporated
216 West 7th Street
St. Paul, MN 55102
1-800-328-8263

Silvo Hardware Company
611 N. Broadway
Milwaukee, WI 53202
1-800-331-1261

Trendlines
375 Beacham Street
Chelsea, MA 01250
1-800-767-9999

Woodcraft
210 Wood County Industrial Park
P.O. Box 1686
Parkersburg, WV 26102
1-800-225-1153

Woodworkers Supply
1108 North Glen Road
Casper, WY 82601
1-800-645-9292

General Suppliers

The Wooden Boat Shop
1007 N.E. Boat Street
Seattle, WA 98105
1-800-933-3600

Doc Freeman's
999 N. Northlake Way
Seattle, WA 98103
1-800 -0423-8641 (800-247-2149 in Washington)

Flounder Bay Boat Lumber
1019 3rd Street
Anacortes, WA 98221
(206) 293-2369

Olson Lumber Company
9300 Aurora N.
Seattle, WA 98103
1-800-533-4381

Seattle Ship Supply
Fishermen's Terminal
Seattle, WA 98119
(206) 283-0830

Fisheries Supply
1900 N. Northlake Way
Seattle, WA 98103
1-800-426-6930

Index

Index

If you enjoyed *A Skiff for All Seasons*, you may be interested in these International Marine books. Prices are subject to change without notice.

The Nature of Boats
Insights and Esoterica for the Nautically Obsessed
by Dave Gerr

Boat noodling.

Boat lovers suffer universally from this benign affliction. In its mildest form boat noodling is nothing more than wondering why that sloop in the next slip is faster than yours. In a more serious manifestation it could mean some earnest daydreaming—drifting off for extended periods, sketching design ideas on the back of an envelope.

Naval architect Dave Gerr offers the perfect antidote, a browser's reference to understanding how boats tick: all you've ever wanted to know about boats—power and sail, race and cruise, dinghy and megayacht.

In the clear, friendly, nontechnical style that has made his column for *Offshore* magazine so enduring and so popular, Gerr explains everything from how thick a hull should be to why one sailboat tips less than another, from choosing an engine to designing a rig for your trawler yacht, from building a dinghy to simple rules of thumb for dozens of design quandaries.

Gerr writes for the boat noodler in us all—those seriously interested in learning and dreaming about all types of watercraft. There is no better way to become a better seaman, equipped to handle any contingency. And there's no better place to start than with *The Nature of Boats*.

Hardbound, 432 pages, 253 illustrations, $29.95, Book No. 60262

Boatowner's Mechanical and Electrical Manual
How to Maintain, Repair, and
Improve Your Boat's Essential Systems
by Nigel Calder

Best-selling author Nigel Calder, a diesel mechanic for more than 20 years, a boatbuilder, and a cabinetmaker, walks the reader through the repair, maintenance, and setting up of the boat's primary systems. Here are the details on the electrical system, electronics equipment, generator sets, solar panels, wind and water generators, the engine, transmission, refrigeration and air conditioning, waste disposal systems, pumps, steering, stoves, heaters, lanterns, spars, standing and running rigging, furling systems—areas on any boat, sail or power, most prone to problems.

"This book should come as standard equipment with every boat." *—SAIL*

"Possibly the most thorough volume on boat maintenance ever produced. It will be an invaluable part of my reference library." *—Better Boat*

"If there's one person in the world I'd choose as a fellow crew member when things malfunction, it'd be Nigel Calder." *—Ocean Navigator*

"A major achievement for both author and publisher. It would be hard to imagine anything going wrong with a boat that couldn't be figured out with this book at hand; the price is a bargain." *—Sailing World*

"An impressive compilation of advice on boat equipment and systems—one of the best we've seen. The drawings are excellent and the text will aid the average boatowner in performing most maintenance and repair jobs, be it testing the engine's alternator or rebuilding an electric pump. Much of the information cannot be found anywhere else." *—Practical Sailor*

"Well worth the price." *—Powerboat Reports*

Hardbound, 544 pages, 600 illustrations, $39.95, Book No. 60128

Buehler's Backyard Boatbuilding
by George Buehler

Everybody has the dream: Build a boat in the backyard and sail off to join the happy campers of Pago Pago, right? But how? Assuming you aren't independently wealthy, if you want a boat that is really you, you gotta build it yourself.

Backyard boatbuilding has its problems. Fiberglass is itchy and smelly. Ferrocement, once the rage, has pretty much sunk from favor. Following the time-honored tradition of the Golden Age of Yachting, with its lovingly crafted intricate joints of rare tropical hardwoods takes a great deal of time. To say nothing of money. The wood/epoxy system means working with stuff that's not exactly benign.

Where does that leave us? In the capable hands of George Buehler, who honors the timeless traditions of the sea all right, but those from the other side of the boatyard tracks. Buehler draws his inspiration from centuries of workboat construction, where semiskilled fishermen built rugged, economical boats from everyday materials in their own backyards, and went to sea in all kinds of weather.

Buehler's boats sail on every ocean and perform every task, from long-term liveaboards in Norwegian fjords to a traveling doctor's office in Alaska. Here are complete plans for seven cruising boats—from a 28-foot sailboat to a 55-foot power cruiser. All the information you need is here, including step-by-step instructions honed by nearly 20 years of supplying boat plans to backyard builders—and helping them out when they get in trouble.

"Everyone will revere this book."   —*The Ensign*

Paperbound, 384 pages, 150 illustrations, $24.95, Book No. 60227

Boatbuilding Manual, Third Edition
by Robert M. Steward

Thousands of amateur boatbuilders have turned to *Boatbuilding Manual* for advice, and it has been used for years as a standard textbook at boatbuilding and design schools. Now, in this new edition, Robert Steward has again thoroughly updated his classic book.

Steward believes that because of a lack of information, many capable people have been denied the joys of boatbuilding. *Boatbuilding Manual* provides that information.

Like its predecessors, this edition is heavily weighted toward traditional wooden construction, but the methods it teaches apply to wooden boat construction of any type, as well as to the building of tooling for fiberglass hulls and to the finishing off of composite fiberglass-wooden boats. The book includes discussions of new techniques, materials, and products, with a particular emphasis on developments in woods and adhesives.

"This is a book at home in the workshop, not the library. Pulled from beneath a pile of shavings, it is just the right thing to help make a tough decision or to quiet an unwelcome advisor."

—*SAIL*

"One of its special merits is the author's direct, sensible, and even cheerful attitude, in short, it is thoroughly practical."   —*Practical Boat Owner*

"The core around which any serious wooden boat building library should be built."
—*WoodenBoat*

Hardbound, 288 pages, 165 illustrations, $29.95, Book No. 60160

Build the New Instant Boats
by Harold "Dynamite" Payson

Harold H. Payson—known to his associates, friends, and his wife as Dynamite—thinks *you* can build a boat. In fact, if you can saw a penciled line, apply glue, drive nails, and bring a modest measure of patience to the task, you can build and launch a smart and able craft in as few as 40 man-hours. You need not be driven by lack of tools, materials, skills, or time to abandon in frustration a project you conceived in a spirit of pleasurable anticipation.

Years ago, when Dynamite began supplementing his boatbuilding work by selling boat plans, he got feedback from a number of customers who found the boats too difficult to build. Many of these would-be boatbuilders had never heard of lofting and were intimidated and discouraged by the necessity of building a jig before building the boat itself. Many of them, too, couldn't find local suppliers of the lumber and other materials called for in the plans.

Selling plans for boats that never got built went against Dynamite's Down East grain, and it was also, he figured, a "straight road to bankruptcy in the long run." He discussed the problem with designer Phil Bolger, who agreed, on one condition, to design a series of boats that would require no lofting, no jig, and no lumber that could not be obtained at any local building-supplies store. Boats that would not require a great investment of time to cut out and button up. In short, boats for the inexperienced builder whose desire is to get out on the water. The one condition was that Dynamite, a member of *Small Boat Journal's* Hall of Fame, build and test each prototype to wring out every bug before offering the plans for sale. The result was a fleet of six boats described in his first book, *Instant Boats.*

Here are eleven new instant boats to choose from, including a 15-foot, double-chine rowing and sailing boat; an 8-foot sailing pram; a 15-foot, double-chine outboard speed boat; and a 16-foot, double-ended, lug-rigged sharpie. Three of the new boats are built with a new "tack-and-tape" method that eliminates most of the beveling and results in a very shapely and spritely craft. Dynamite writes of everything you'll need to know to build one of his boats with common sense and uncommon good humor. Then you can start right in.

Pleasant sailing.

Paperbound, 160 pages, 92 photos, 33 plans, $19.95, Book No. 60230

Ultralight Boatbuilding
How You Can Build Light, Elegant, and Simple Boats
Using Plywood and Epoxy
by Thomas J. Hill

Ultralight canoes and small boats are things of beauty, their apparent delicacy concealing great strength. They are lapstrake-constructed from marine plywood planks, each plank overlapping the one below it in a gracefully curved hull. Epoxy glue along the laps gives the hull structural reinforcement, minimizing the need for framing and permitting an amazingly light structure. Round-bilged and elegant, they are built over jigs, but the method is straightforward and not time consuming. You can build a boat that will give you fun and satisfaction, one you can be proud of, in a winter of leisurely weekends. No fancy tools are needed, and care and patience will make up for whatever you lack in woodworking skills.

Tom Hill, the chief proponent of ultralight building and its leading practitioner, describes the method from start to finish using a skiff and canoe as examples. In the appendix is a gallery of ultralight designs, all but one of which you can build without lofting. If you want more flexibility, however, you can adapt almost any lapstrake small-boat design, traditional or modern, to the ultralight method. With some lofting (directions for which are given) you may then build a wide range of boats whose offsets are available. And you may adjust planking thickness and scantlings to give your boat extremely light weight with normal strength, or moderate weight with great strength.

Particularly if you lack an extensively equipped workshop and professional skills, *Ultralight Boatbuilding* will unlock exciting possibilities you considered out of reach.

"Very thorough and properly inspiring . . . an intelligent mix of traditional design and modern technique."
—*Whole Earth Review*

Paperbound, 144 pages, 140 illustrations, $17.95, Book No. 60951

Skiffs & Schooners
R.D. "Pete" Culler

There is nothing else quite like *Skiffs & Schooners*, and there never will be. This book offers the chance to sit for a while with a master shipbuilder and soak up his knowledge and wisdom on every facet of small boats and boatbuilding: how to choose and work wood, what boats serve what purpose, how to finish a boat, how to fit her out, how to build oars, how to design and fashion a small-boat rig. First published in 1974, *Skiffs & Schooners* galvanized the renaissance of small craft that was then in its infancy.

Skiffs & Schooners lapsed from print in 1985, another victim of a decade of self-indulgences and instant gratification on a scale Pete Culler could never have countenanced. Now that guzzling gas and borrowing from the future are once again passing from fashion, perhaps some small corner of our collective imagination will turn again to gracing our waterways with simple, stout boats that arrest the gaze, soothe the soul, and dissipate rather than fulfill the restive urge to always be somewhere else doing some other things.

The simple things are still the best. May this book enrich your boating, and your decade.

"The author has rendered a profound service to wooden boat enthusiasts and students of wooden boat building arts by sharing with us a knowledge that is rapidly become extinct. This book is a must for anyone who takes the subject seriously."   —*Yachting*

Paperbound, 208 pages, 180 illustrations, $19.95, Book No. 60186

The Fiberglass Boat Repair Manual
Allan H. Vaitses

Are there hairline cracks in your boat's deck or topsides gelcoat? Have her color and luster faded over the years? Does she have deck leaks? Has she been holed? Is her hull oilcanning in a sea? If your answer to any of these questions is yes, this book is for you. This is the definitive guide for fiberglass boat repair and beautification, covering not just cosmetic dings and scratches, but also major repairs of structural damage to hulls and decks. It will show you how to:

- replace deteriorated gelcoat, or repair the flaws in an existing gelcoat and recoat it with polyurethane and marine alkyd enamel paint
- strengthen a weak and overly flexible hull or deck
- tab in loose hull liners and joinerwork
- make templates from the good side of a hull to reshape large shattered or missing areas on the other side
- repair or replace water-saturated deck cores
- repair keels, rudders, and centerboards
- rebed and refasten underwater and on-deck hardware
- rebed, refasten, and strengthen hull-to-deck joints
- fix broken hatches, and make new ones when necessary
- treat the symptoms and causes of overstressed hulls

In short, *The Fiberglass Boat Repair Manual* will be an invaluable source of advice as you maintain and restore your boat, and it should encourage many would-be-but-for-lack-of-funds boatowners to buy one of the thousands of damaged boats available at little cost and make her "like new" once again. As the author says, one of the great things about a fiberglass boat is that no damage is beyond repair, no matter how crippling it may appear, and the only skills needed are patience, ingenuity, common sense, and a good eye.

"The aroma of resin wafting out of this manual is refreshing. The book will save you money and grief before you can say woven roving."   —*Sailing*

Hardbound, 192 pages, 200 illustrations, with four-page color insert, $29.95, Book No. 60530

Look for These and Other International Marine Books
at Your Local Bookstore

To Order Call Toll Free 1-800-822-8158
(outside the U.S., call 717-794-2191)

or write to International Marine, A Division of TAB Books,
Blue Ridge Summit, PA 17294-0840.

- -

Title	Product No.	Quantity	Price

Subtotal: $_____

Postage and Handling: $_____

($3.00 in U.S., $5.00 outside U.S.): $_____

Add applicable state and local sales tax: $_____

TOTAL: $_____

❑Check or money order made payable to TAB Books

Charge my   ❑VISA   ❑MasterCard   ❑American Express

Acct. No._____ Exp._____

Signature:_____

Name:_____

Address:_____

City:_____

State:_____   Zip:_____

International Marine catalog free with purchase; otherwise send $1.00 in check or
money order and receive $1.00 credit on your next purchase.

Orders outside U.S. must pay with international money order in U.S. dollars.

**If for any reason you are not satisfied with the book(s) you order, simply return
it (them) within 15 days and receive a full refund.**